Indiana9 Fossils

(For All Your Fossil Needs)

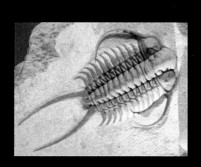

www.indiana9fossils.com

Fossil News

The Journal of Avocational Paleontology
Vol. 20.4 — Winter 2017

FRONT COVER: A rare and exquisitely preserved specimen of *Saniwa ensidens*, an extinct monitor lizard. Found and prepped by Tony Lindgren. Photo © Tom Wiewandt; used by permission. BACK COVER: A large palm frond, found and prepped by Robert Bowen. The original now resides in the Mace Brown Museum of Natural History at the College of Charleston. Photo © Robert Bowen; used by permission.

CONTRIBUTORS TO THIS ISSUE

ANDY SECHER (writer) is a Field Associate in Paleontology with the American Museum of Natural History in New York. His specialty is trilobites, and he currently edits the AMNH's renowned trilobite website—a site that also features photos drawn from his personal trilobite collection, which houses over 6,000 specimens from locales around the globe. He is currently finishing a book on the subject called *Travels with Trilobites* which will feature insights on his excursions to many of the world's leading Paleozoic locations.

JOE CANTRELL (writer) Tahlequah, Oklahoma, High School drafted Joe Cantrell as school photographer in 1960, when he was 14. He served twice as a Naval officer in Vietnam then spent sixteen years as a photojournalist in Asia, trying to understand. Always interested in rocks, fossils, and fractals, Cantrell has worked the last five years on focus-stacking microphotography. The worlds, little and big, so revealed make him feel like the fourteen-year-old discovering the unsuspected.

LANCE GRANDE (writer) is the Negaunee Distinguished Service Curator in the Integrative Research Center of the Field Museum in Chicago. He specializes in evolutionary biology and comparative anatomy through four major areas of research: the community paleoecology of North America during the early Cenozoic, particularly in Fossil Basin, Wyoming; the evolutionary biology and biogeography of ray-finned fishes; the comparative anatomy of vertebrates; and the methods and philosophy of science. The author of numerous books and hundreds of articles, Grande has directed a particularly active field program in the famous Green River Formation of Wyoming for more than three decades and is a leading authority for this region.

PHOTOGRAPHERS AND ARTISTS: **Michelle Tibbetts** is the owner of Michelle Tibbetts Photography. Originally from the east coast, she moved to Wyoming after graduating from the University of Massachusetts. Michelle is passionate about life and enjoys photographing people, landscapes, and wildlife. She lives off the grid with her family near Kemmerer, Wyoming. When she isn't exploring the outdoors with her family, she works as a photojournalist and reporter for the *Kemmerer Gazette*. **PalaeoArt (Tom Sermon)** is an artist who focuses exclusively on producing original illustrations of fossilized remains of prehistoric creatures. Having studied at Oxford University, England, he is attempting to bring back the classic style of scientific illustrations but with modern media and techniques. What's unique is that instead of selling his originals, he trades his original art for fossils to add to his collection. He can be reached at tom@palaeo-art.com or visit www.palaeo-art.com. **Thomas Wiewandt**, owner of Wild Horizons Productions (wildhorizons.com), is a professional natural history photographer devoted to art and education. He earned degrees in zoology (M.S., U. Arizona) and ecology (Ph.D., Cornell) and has been active in ecotourism, publishing, and filmmaking. His award-winning work has been featured on PBS and in many books, calendars, and magazines worldwide. For twenty-seven years, he has photographed prize fossil specimens, a project destined to become a book.

HOW TO SUBSCRIBE: Domestic US rates: $50.00 USD for four quarterly issues, payable via PayPal (FossilNews@FourCatsPress.com) or Venmo (@FourCatsPress). Outside the U.S., please contact us for a quote. Single issues: $16.00 USD (plus postage if outside the US). Complete info at: tinyurl.com/fnsubscribe.

DISPLAY ADVERTISING: Subscribers receive 10% off display advertising. Our current "Rate Sheet & Specifications" are online at: tinyurl.com/fnadvertise.

EDITOR/PUBLISHER: Wendell Ricketts CONTRIBUTING EDITORS: Diana Fattori & Nando Musmarra EDITOR EMERITA: Lynne Clos FOUNDING EDITOR: Joe Small

SUBMISSION GUIDELINES: *Fossil News* welcomes submissions from all those with an interest in paleontology and fossil collecting. Submissions and queries to: FossilNews@FourCatsPress.com.

HOW TO SUBMIT YOUR WORK: Please read our guidelines (tinyurl.com/fnguidelines) or contact us for details.

BOOK REVIEWS: *Fossil News* does not accept unsolicited or previously published reviews. It's always best to query first. If possible, send clips of your published work.

EDITING AND REVISION: *Fossil News* reserves the right to edit submissions for length, grammar, punctuation, structure, and style.

PAYMENT: We offer contributors a complimentary copy of the issue in which their work appears and a choice of (a) two insertions of a display ad (up to one-half page) or (b) 50% off an annual or gift subscription.

Fossil News
The Journal of Avocational Paleontology
FossilNews@FourCatsPress.com
www.FossilNews.org

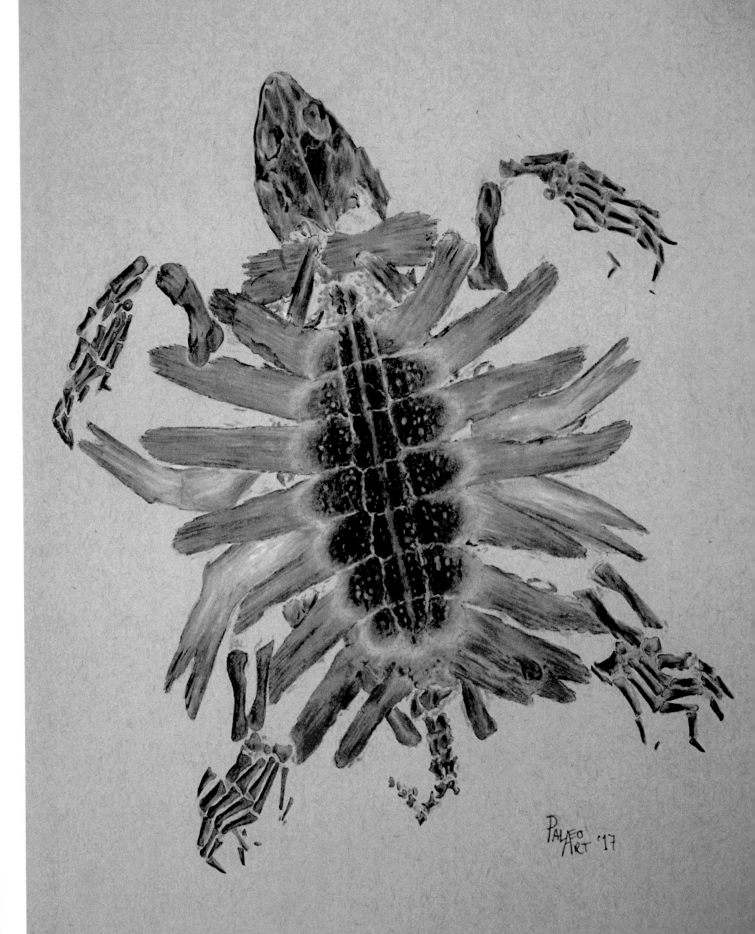

PALEO
Art '17

Kemmerer, Wyoming: Gateway to PaleoTourism, U.S.A.

Surrounded by high desert and even higher mountains, the tiny hamlet of Kemmerer, Wyoming, on the southwestern edge of the state, began life in 1897 as a coal town. It still is one today—the Westmoreland company operates a large mining operation west of town—but Kemmerer is also one of the best places in the U.S. to set up base camp for a vacation that includes fishing, golf, national parks, camping, off-roading and snowmobiling, picture-postcard lakes, bird and wildlife watching, the majesty and peacefulness of the great outdoors—and, of course, the astounding and beautiful Green River fossils that are famous all over the world.

Kemmerer has some historical "firsts" to boast of, too. It's the home of the original J. C. Penney store founded in 1902 (the store is still open for business—and to visitors—today); William L. Carlisle, meanwhile, one of America's last train robbers, lived in Kemmerer after being paroled from the state penitentiary in 1936, and he opened a newsstand and cigar shop there. If you like a slightly obscure literary reference, Kemmerer was also the model for Philip K. Dick's "Old Town," the setting of his dystopian 1959 science fiction novel, *Time Out of Joint*.

Most people, though, come to Kemmerer less for the history and more for the *prehistory*. For a town of just under 2,800 souls (3,540, if you count the 1.2 square miles of Diamondville directly to the south and connected to Kemmerer, aptly enough, by Fossil Road), Kemmerer boasts more rock-and-fossil shops per capita than any other American town (see p. 28). It's also home to Fossil Butte National Monument and its terrific museum (see pp. 17-24) as well as to an assortment of commercial fossil quarries where visitors of all ages can "split rock" and find the fossils of fish and other organisms that once lived in and around the long-vanished Eocene-era lake now known as "Fossil Lake" (see pp. 6-15).

This issue of *Fossil News* is a special in-depth look at the Fossil Basin area, where Kemmerer sits, and a guide to where to go, what to do, and how to load yourself up with fossils before you head back home.

This issue would not have been possible without the quarry operators who opened up their dig sites and workshops to *Fossil News*, especially Robert Bowen and Jennifer Edinger, Rick Hebdon and Candi Mondy, Tony Lindgren, Seth Sorensen and Patrick Hogle, and Shirley Ulrich; the fossil-gallery owners and staff who freely shared so much information; the photographers and artists who lent their work; the rangers of the Fossil Butte National Monument; Dana and Mike Stroud; Dr. Lance Grande; and Kemmerer City Manager Andrew Nelson and the Fossil Basin Promotion Board.

Facing page: A drawing in Prismacolor pencil by PalaeoArt (Tom Sermon) of the superb fossil of a soft-shelled turtle, Axestemys byssinus. *The actual fossil, discovered by Tony Lindgren in Fossil Lake deposits, is of a juvenile and is only about four inches long. © The artist; used by permission. This page: Two fossil fish on a single slab from Adam Lindgren's quarry. Original photo © Michelle Tibbetts; used by permission. "Gyotaku" effect by Fossil News.*

In the Beginning: An Excerpt from Lance Grande's *The Lost World of Fossil Lake*

Every story must have a beginning, and this one starts in the middle of the Cretaceous period, about ninety million years ago. By that time, rising sea levels had created the great Western Interior Seaway, dividing the North American continent into distinct eastern and western subcontinents that would remain separated for the next twenty-five million years. This immense marine waterway was 762 meters (2,500 feet) deep and hundreds of miles wide in places. It connected the Arctic Ocean in the north to the Gulf of Mexico in the south, and it served as an impenetrable barrier to the dispersal of most freshwater and terrestrial plants and animals between the eastern and western North American subcontinents. The effects of this long continental division—together with a solid land connection between the western subcontinent and Asia—greatly influenced the early development of the North American fauna and flora. The bio-geographic influence from Asia was still very strong in the Eocene Green River Formation of western North America.

Time Changes Everything

The widespread, massive extinction at the end of the Cretaceous wiped out an estimated 75% of all living species on the planet. The great seaway disappeared and, along with it, all pterosaurs, marine reptiles, ammonites, and dinosaurs became extinct, except for a single surviving dinosaurian lineage: birds. In the Early Cenozoic, however, Earth's biota was in the process of renewing itself in a different form. The age of mammals arrived on land with a vengeance and overtook the long rule of reptiles. Flowering plants and broad-leafed trees diversified, as did the animals that pollinated and fed on them. Birds and bats were also becoming more diverse and now controlled a sky devoid of pterosaurs. Teleost fishes (the group containing 95% of all

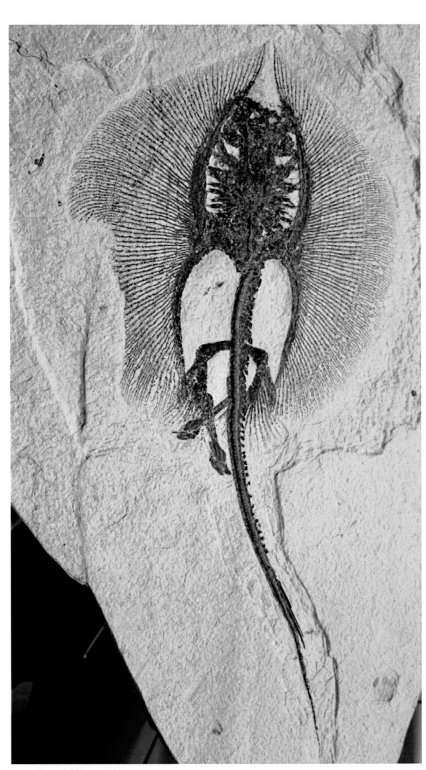

One of the many specatcular Heliobatis radians *rays to come from Fossil Lake quarries. This specimen, collected and prepped by Robert Bowen from the American Quarry, shows what appears to be a bite out of its left fin, which was perhaps the cause of its death. Photo © Michelle Tibbetts; used by permission.*

living fishes today) expanded their dominance in both marine and freshwater environments, and numerous freshwater lake systems formed in the eastern part of a North American continent no longer divided by a seaway.

One of the most remarkable western lake systems to appear was the Early Cenozoic Green River Lake System. This great lake complex [comprised] three lakes at its peak: Lake Uinta, Lake Gosiute, and our subject here: Fossil Lake. The earliest appearance of this lake system began in the late Paleocene as a result of regional uplift, and the lake system eventually formed from thousands of years of drainage and runoff. This was a true great lake system with one of the longest durations of any known lake system on Earth. One of its lakes, Lake Uinta, lasted well over ten million years. The North American Great Lake System that exists today is only about 10,000 years old.

Although the Green River Lake System persisted over a period of millions of years, it was not a continuously stable freshwater environment for all of that time. Geological evidence indicates that all three of its lakes went through drying phases in which shorelines fluctuated wildly, and salinity concentrations rose to levels lethal to most freshwater fish species. The few species of fishes and other freshwater aquatic organisms that survived such periods must have retreated up the tributaries that fed the lakes. Some probably just became extinct, because the aquatic diversity of freshwater fishes achieved within the FBM is never seen again in the Green River Lake System.

The long-buried sedimentary rocks of the Green River Lake System, particularly the Fossil Butte Member (FBM) of southwestern Wyoming, deposited by the middle phase of Fossil Lake, provide a window into the deep past. In particular, the FBM

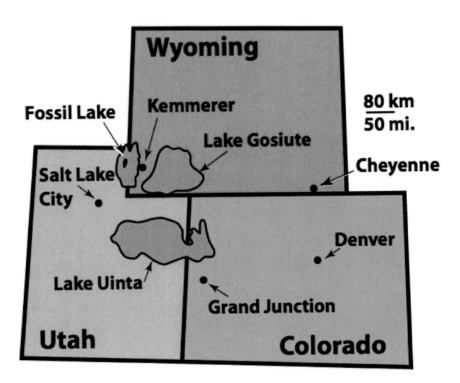

provides the earliest comprehensive look at a post-dinosaur community in graphic detail. A few younger members within the Green River Formation show great diversity of insect and plant fossils, but they lack the overall biotic diversity known from the FBM.

The Larger Stratigraphic Context: The Relationship of the FBM to the Other Thirteen Members of the Green River Formation

The great longevity of the Green River Lake System (particularity Lake Uinta) makes the Green River Formation one of the largest documented accumulations of lake sediments in the world. This enormous formation extends over an area of more than 65,000 square kilometers (25,000 square miles), and over much of its geographic expanse it is 600 meters (2,000 feet) or more in thickness.

Today the Green River Formation is divided into fourteen different subdivisions called members. Each of the three lakes that created the formation had a different duration. Lake Uinta—whose lithified sediments are located in the Uinta Basin of Utah and the Piceance Basin of Colorado—

was the largest of the three. It was the first to form and the last to disappear and is today represented by six members. From youngest to oldest, these deposits are known as the Parachute Creek Member, the Garden Gulch Member, the Douglas Creek Member, the Anvil Point Member, the Cow Ridge Member, and the Flagstaff Member. Lake Uinta was lagoonal to very shallow lacustrine, represented today by mudstones, sandstones, siltstones, and shales. Eventually, in the latest part of the Paleocene, Lake Uinta dried up in its southern end while expanding eastward into what is now Uinta Basin in Utah and Piceance Basin in Colorado. At the same time, Lake Gosiute and Fossil Lake were forming in Wyoming. The sedimentary rock left by Lake Uinta represents one of the thickest documented accumulations of lake sediments in the world, and the shales left by Lake Uinta are rich in fossil fuels, containing an estimated one trillion barrels of oil. The sedimentary rocks from Lake Uinta don't contain a very diverse vertebrate fauna, but they do contain some of the most productive plant and insect fossil localities within its Parachute Creek Member, near Douglas Pass, Colorado, and Bonanza, Utah.

Lake Gosiute, whose lithified sediments are found in Green River Basin directly east of Fossil Basin, was the second largest of the Green River lakes. Its deposits formed five different members in the Green River Formation (from youngest to oldest): the Laney Member, the Wilkins

freshwater, indicated by abundant catfishes (Ictaluridae) and suckers (Catostomidae), two primary, bottom-dwelling freshwater families of fishes. Both are curiously absent from the FBM deposits, probably due either to ecological conditions (Fossil Lake possibly being less hospitable to bottom dwellers than Lake Gosiute) or differing age (the FBM deposits are about three million years older than the Laney Member deposits).

The third lake represented by the Green River Formation was Fossil Lake. At its peak, Fossil Lake also extended into the northeastern corner of what is now Utah and the southeastern corner of what is now Idaho. This lake was also called the "Unnamed Green River Lake West of Gosiute Lake" by Wilmot Hyde Bradley, Chief Geologist of the U.S. Geological Survey in 1948, and "Fossil Syncline Lake" by Paul Orman McGrew and Michael Casilliano in their 1975 *The Geological History of Fossil Butte National Monument and Fossil Basin*. Fossil Lake is represented in the Green River Formation by three members: the Angelo Member (the youngest), the Fossil Butte Member, and the Road Hollow Member (the oldest). The Road Hollow Member represents the earliest formation of Fossil Lake and is the thickest of the three members, while the Angelo Member records the latest phase and eventual demise of Fossil Lake. In the Angelo phase, the lake became saline, and there was a general disappearance of fish and other aquatic organisms. The thinnest and most fossiliferous, the Fossil Butte Member, ranges from only about twenty-two meters in thickness in the nearshore deposits to about twelve meters in

The "Sandwich Beds" at American Quarry show the vertical interbanding that may represent storms, volcanic eruptions, floods, or other events in the ancient history of Fossil Lake. The darker, lower band in this photo is known as the "Tri-Ash Layer," interpreted as the volcanic ash deposited by three eruptions in rapid succession. Photo © Wendell Ricketts; all rights reserved.

Peak Member, the Fontanelle Member, the Tipton Shale Member, and the Luman Member. Longer-lived than Fossil Lake, but shorter-lived than Lake Uinta, Lake Gosiute is thought to have been shallow with a fluctuating shoreline throughout its history. During periods of contraction, the lake often became saline, and the fishes retreated to freshwater tributaries, marshes, and ponds that fringed the lake. There were also periods during which the lake was

thickness in the mid-lake quarries, and it represents only about 9% of the stratigraphic thickness of the Fossil Lake deposits.

Sweet Spot in the Eocene: The Relatively Short but Productive Duration of the FBM

The FBM is a tiny slice of the Green River Formation. To put it in perspective, the Green River Lake system lasted at least twelve million years, Fossil Lake appears to have lasted for less than two million of those years, and the Fossil Butte Member probably represents only a few tens of thousands of years at most, which in the context of geologic time is a blink of an eye.

The known aquatic biodiversity of the FBM exceeds that of the other thirteen members of the Green River Formation combined. This is probably due in part to the variety of well-preserved habitats in these deposits and to the

intense level of fossil excavation from the Fossil Butte Member over the years. In a 1994 work, my colleague Paul Buchheim and I estimated that over half a million fossil fish were excavated by commercial quarries between 1970 and 1994 and that another million incomplete or damaged fish were excavated and discarded during the same period. I estimate that over 200,000 specimens are now excavated annually. After more than a century of collection, millions of fossils have been recovered from the FBM, so even proportionately rare elements of the fauna and flora (e.g., birds, bats, etc.) are now known by numerous specimens. And the diversity continues to climb.

Within the FBM, some of the most productive fossil localities are located within a relatively narrow zone of limestone that includes the "18-inch layer" and the underlying "sandwich beds," together representing what is probably only a few thousand years of the lake's history. Other highly productive zones are the so-called "mini-fish beds" near the K-spar tuff bed. It is the K-spar tuff that has been radiometrically dated to be about 51.97 million years old.

From Lake Muck to Limestone: The FBM Matrix

Because the mountains surrounding Fossil Lake contained significant amounts of limestone ($CaCO_3$), the streams flowing down their slopes became super rich in dissolved calcium carbonate before reaching the lake. As these streams filled the lake basin, Fossil Lake became supersaturated with calcium carbonate (the principal component of limestone). Like air supersaturated with moisture resulting in rain, the water column would periodically "rain" calcium carbonate, which accumu-

lated on the lake bottom as a lime ooze. For such a thing to have occurred, the lake must have been somewhat alkaline. As lake-bottom sediments accumulated to hundreds of feet thick during the early part of the Eocene, the enormous weight of the upper sediments compressed and dewatered the lower sediments, eventually turning them into limestone. The extreme compression that converted the ooze into limestone also helped flatten the fossilizing organisms along the bedding plane. Starting in the middle Eocene, the lake dried up and the region continued to rise in elevation, reversing the process of deposition to one of erosion. Over the next thirty to forty million years, the region was eroded to a series of buttes, exposing portions of the Fossil Lake limestone. Erosion continued around the buttes, creating the huge valleys between them. Today all that remains of Fossil Lake lies near the tops of the isolated buttes that were spared from erosion.

Three Mother Lodes of the FBM: The 18-inch Layer, the Sandwich Beds, and the Mini-Fish Beds

The two layers within the FBM that have produced the most celebrated "mother lodes" of fossils are the 18-inch layer (also referred to as the "F-1" or "black-fish" layer) and the underlying "sandwich bed" layer (also referred to as the "F-2," "split-fish," or "orange-fish" layer where it crops out near the shoreline in the region of Thompson Ranch). More recently, a third highly fossiliferous layer near the K-spar ruff beds has been mined for fossils, the so-called "mini-fish beds."

The rock exposures of the FBM were prominent features of the topography surrounding the town of Fossil

Lance Grande's U. Chicago team working the 18-inch layer at the Tynsky Quarry. Grande is in the straw hat, far left. Photo © Michelle Tibbetts; used by permission.

and its railroad station. The mid-lake 18-inch layer averages about a half meter in thickness (thus the common name "18-inch layer"). In contrast, the nearshore sandwich beds are several meters in thickness. The sandwich beds also occur in the mid-lake quarries below the 18-inch layer, but the fish there are darker in color with less of an orange tint than those in the nearshore localities. The sandwich beds in the mid-lake quarries are also thinner than in the nearshore quarries due to higher sedimentation rates near shore.

The laminated limestones of these highly fossiliferous layers split cleanly along bedding planes, producing slabs of rock with very flat surfaces. The brown to orange-brown fossils embedded in the lighter-hued limestone slabs are so beautifully preserved that they sometimes resem-

ble wildlife portraits. The 18-inch and sandwich layers are not only packed full of well-preserved fossils; they are also among the easiest rock layers within the FBM from which to remove large quantities of easy-to-prepare fossils. Today, about forty square kilometers of 18-inch and sandwich-bed layers remain on a mixture of private, state, and federal lands.

The reason that the 18-inch layer around Fossil Butte is sometimes called the "black-fish layer" is because fossils are often preserved with black bones and dark brown scales, and are darker in color than those from the nearshore sandwich beds of the Thompson Ranch region. The 18-inch layer deposits are also strongly demarcated in cross section with alternating light and dark bands, or laminations. The light bands are pure carbonate rock, and

the dark bands consist of kerogen, an organic-rich material from decomposed microorganisms. The couplets of light and dark laminations were previously thought to represent annual cycles of Fossil Lake resulting from seasonal water turnover. If the couplets had been annual markers, that would indicate that the 18-inch layer was deposited over a period of several thousand years. But more recent work has shown that the frequency of lamination couplets within equivalent stratigraphic levels varies significantly between the mid-lake and the nearshore deposits of the FBM; so at least some of them cannot possibly represent annual cycles. In addition, the remarkable preservation of large skeletons with all bones in normal position suggests a much more rapid burial process. The couplets may actually represent more frequent events such as periodic storms, major variations in lake inflow, periodic die-offs of microorganisms, or other common environmental events that happened more than once per year. We will probably never know for sure what the exact duration was for the deposition of all the 18-inch layer sediments, but the 18-inch and underlying sandwich layers together likely represent a period lasting as long as several thousand years or as short as a few hundred. We can tell that this period was one of relative ecological stability in Fossil Lake, because so many of the lake's aquatic species are present from the lowest part of the sandwich beds to the uppermost part of the 18-inch layer. The sandwich bed period of deposition also represents the maximum-area extent of Fossil Lake.

The excellent preservation of the lamination couplets in the midlake 18-inch layer and the rarity of bottom-dwelling species there (e.g., stingrays, decapods, and mollusks) suggest that Fossil Lake may have had a stratified water column at its center, with well-oxygenated surface water (epilimnion) and stagnant, lethal bottom waters (hypolimnion).

Bottom-dwelling fish other than *Notogoneus* could not tolerate the stagnant bottom waters in the mid-lake regions and thus were rare or absent there. Organic material and dead animals that sank from the upper regions would have been relatively protected from scavenging long enough to become buried and well preserved as fossils.

The typical nearshore sandwich layer is several meters in thickness. Bottom-dwelling organisms (e.g., stingrays, crayfish, shrimps, and gastropods) are more common in this layer than in the 18-inch layer. The nearshore sandwich beds of the Thompson Ranch region are also sometimes referred to as the "split-fish beds" because of the manner in which many of the layer's fish have been exposed, particularly in the early years of quarry operations. Smaller fish, in particular, often "split out" in these beds as a "part and counterpart." Splitting out is usually not a good thing for the fossils, because it generally damages the fossil, pulling part of it onto each of the two split surfaces. Early in the history of commercial collecting, split fish were thought to be a boon for business because it was a "two-for-one," and, for rarer pieces, each side could have its missing pieces painted in. In recent years, commercial preparation has become much more sophisticated and detailed, and for anything but the most common species, splits are not desirable nor are heavily restored pieces. In fact, if a rare specimen like a bird, mammal, or turtle is found as a split, the part and counterpart are sometimes glued back together and the piece is prepared from one or both of the exposed sides.

The different FBM quarry sites provide comparative paleontological samples contrasting the nearshore versus farther offshore aquatic communities of Eocene Fossil Lake. The known species of the mid-lake 18-inch layer are largely the same as those from nearshore sandwich beds. The main diversity and paleoecological differences between the nearshore and mid-lake fossils are in relative proportion of species and size classes. In the mid-lake 18-inch deposits, stingrays, crayfish, shrimps, *Goniobasis* snails, baby fish for many FBM species, mooneyes (*Hiodon*), trout-perches (*Amphiplaga*), and the mollusk-eating gar *Masillosteus* are much rarer than in the sandwich beds. The nearshore sandwich beds produce more mammals, birds, schools of

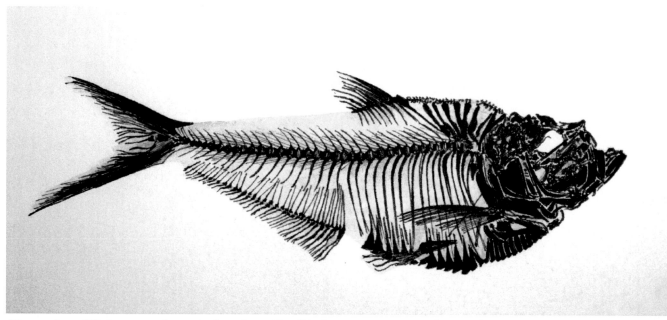

Illustration of Diplomystus dentatus, *based on a Fossil Lake specimen. Original art work © Tom Sermon ; used by permission.*

juvenile fish, and young turtles, and have far fewer *Priscacara* and a complete absence of *Notogoneus*. We can see the effects of the different ecological habitats within Fossil Lake on the distribution of its inhabitants. For example, nearshore habitats were generally better suited as nurseries for young aquatic organisms as they are today. Well-oxygenated bottom waters near shore were better suited for stingrays and other bottom-dwelling organisms. And, of course, flightless land animals fell into the lake at its edge rather than its center.

The 18-inch and sandwich bed layers are close enough to each other in geologic time that they represent a relatively contemporaneous sample. There is also another extremely fossiliferous layer located near the K-spar tuff bed, sometimes referred to as the "mini-fish beds," that produces extremely large quantities of common fish species (*Knightia*, small *Diplomystus*, and small *Mioplosus*). This layer also produces the greatest abundance of the paddlefish *Crossopholis*, although even here *Crossopholis* is a proportionately rare element.

The World of Fossil Lake as Illustrated in the FBM: A Transitional North American Biota

Early Eocene southwestern Wyoming was as different from today's world as it was from its Cretaceous predecessor. Fifty-two million years ago, southwestern Wyoming contained lake-basin lowlands with a warm, wet, subtropical environment surrounded by highlands and mountains containing pine and other more temperate highland flora. There were active volcanoes to the north of Fossil Lake, as evidenced by ash beds (K-spar tuff) that are thickest in the north part of the lake, thinning to the south. Fossil Lake was home to a large freshwater lake system and a diverse community, including many already ancient families and orders on their way to extinction, as well as early representatives of what would diversify over time into major families and orders of animals and plants living today. There were palm trees, balloon vines, crocodiles, alligators, monitor lizards, boa constrictors, parrots, and a whole community of tropical and subtropical and warm temperate organisms. Sea level was still somewhat higher than it is today, and the warmer, more humid climate was not only regional but global.

Looking at the FBM as an Extinct Community

The diversity and abundance of fossilized contemporaneous species throughout the 18-inch and underlying sandwich layers allow us to study not only the species' biodiversity, but also interactions that took place among the extinct species within the community. It is the best picture of life in the early Eocene that has ever been discovered. We can see species that were eaten by other species and preserved as stomach contents or fossilized in the moment they were being swallowed by a predator. We can see leaves with chew marks and the insects that might have been eating them. We can see which fish species were schooling, and we can compute ratios of predator versus prey species. We can study size-classes of fish in mass mortalities, or see which species and size-classes were typically nearshore dwellers and which were typically mid-lake dwellers. For many fish species, we can find complete growth series ranging from hatchlings to large adults. Even the process of reproduction is revealed by fossil stingrays: some preserved in mating position, some with

embryos still inside, and others next to newborn offspring. We also find fossilized fecal matter (coprolites) with bone and other materials indicating food items.

A Typical Day in the Field

Most of the FBM fossil quarries lie about ten miles west of the coal-mining town of Kemmerer. Kemmerer and its neighboring town, Diamondville, comprise the self-proclaimed "Fossil Fish Capital of the World," as touted on local road signs.

There are numerous full-time commercial FBM quarries, mostly within the 18-inch layer and sandwich bed horizons, and FBM fossils occur on private land, railroad land, and state land, as well as land governed by the Bureau of Land Management, the Forest Service, and the National Park Service. Without special permits, it is not legal to dig FBM fossils anywhere except on private land with permission of the landowner.

Each summer my field crew—Field Museum preparators, volunteers, students, and myself—packs up the museum trucks and heads west to southwestern Wyoming for a couple of weeks of quarrying in the FBM. It is something I still look forward to after all these years, because every year is different and filled with the anticipation of exploration and discovery. We never know what will be under the next slab of limestone we pry up. All we know is that whatever it is, it hasn't seen the light of day for 52 million years.

"World Fossil Capital." Highway sign on outskirts of Kemmerer, Wyoming. Photo © Wendell Ricketts; all rights reserved.

We work in a five-acre section of the Lewis Ranch quarry leased to commercial quarrier Jim E. Tynsky, where we have enjoyed digging privileges for over two and a half decades. During that time, my numerous team members and I have mined thousands of fossil fishes and a host of other fossil animals and plants out of the Wyoming butte, establishing the Field Museum as the world's largest, most comprehensive collection of FBM fossils.

The quarry lies in the high mountain desert about 2,165 meters (7,100 feet) above sea level. It takes some of our Midwestern crew a day or two to adjust to labor at high altitude and low oxygen levels, but once our bodies have produced a few extra red blood ceils, the excitement of the dig takes over. To hit the dry season and avoid the rains, we make the trip in late June and early July. The quarry cannot be efficiently worked in the rain, and lightning storms can be hazardous because our tents

and vehicles are the highest points on the butte. Summer temperatures can swing widely, typically ranging from around 40°F at night to 90°F in the heat of the day. There are no trees on the butte, so the only shade is from the trucks and rock exposures. Sunscreen, hats, sunglasses, and regular hydration are essential. Still, it is a sharply clean air we breathe and stunningly beautiful landscape that surrounds us. Antelope and deer roam the valley below us, golden and bald eagles soar overhead, and mountain bluebirds fly in and out of their nests in the quarry walls. In the evening the stars are intense and sharply defined, and the moonlight is so bright you can read by it. The outdoor physical labor is spiritually cleansing for those of us who spend so much of our time at computer screens, microscopes, and office meetings for the rest of the year.

Fossil excavation is a mix of force and finesse. Bulldozers remove about nine meters (thirty feet) of over-

Left, Lance Grande's The World of Fossil Lake: Snapshots from Deep Time, *his 2013 "Bible" for Fossil Lake collectors and quarriers. The excerpt here is taken from the introductory chapters of* Fossil Lake, *and we are grateful to Dr. Grande and to his publisher for permission to use this excerpt. At right:* Curators: Behind the Scenes at Natural History Museums, *Grande's most recent book. Both are published by the University of Chicago Press.*

---

burden to get near the top of the 18-inch layer. Then hand-wielded sledgehammers, pry bars, and sturdy shovels are used to remove the next thirteen to fifteen centimeters (five to six inches) of hard, oily, dark gray "capping rock." This is hard work that takes the first day or two of the trip, dreaded by field veterans and eye-opening for beginners. The tough capping rock smells like oil when you smash it, and it has helped protect the lighter colored fossiliferous limestone layers from weathering over the millennia. Once the upper capping layer is removed, the finely laminated, lighter-colored layers of the 18-inch layer are exposed. We sweep the surface clean and check for signs of fossils in the angled sunlight that falls across the slab's surface and remove the fossils that we find. We work through the entire 18-inch layer one layer at a time, hammering sharpened flat shovels and strips of thin spring steel into the layer edges to take advantage of naturally occurring separations along the bedding planes. If the rock is dry and splitting properly, it lifts up in large sheets between two and five centimeters (0.8 and two inches) in thickness. Once a slab is lifted, we check for

fossils on its underside as well as on the newly exposed surface below. A very thin layer of matrix usually covers the fossils, which can be both a blessing and a curse. The matrix will protect the fossils as they are sent back to the museum, but it can also hide small fossils if the sun is directly overhead. Angled sunlight is necessary to cast defining shadows from the underlying fossils on the light-colored rock. For this reason, work in the quarry is suspended between 11:30 a.m. and about 3:30 p.m., when the sun is near directly overhead.

Finding fossils is a different sort of operation in the nearshore sandwich bed quarries of Thompson Ranch. The fossiliferous layer is much thicker than the mid-lake 18-inch layer. The slabs also come up in thicker pieces that split more easily, and prospecting involves re-splitting slabs with a hammer and chisel rather than taking up broad sheets of rock off the quarry floor. Large fishes with a thin covering of matrix can be found in the sandwich beds, just as they are in the 18-inch layer, and once prepared these fishes are some of the most beautiful.

When fossils are found in either the 18-inch layer or the sandwich beds, they are marked and cut out with a gasoline-powered, diamond-blade rock saw. The cut slabs are sized to fit carefully in custom-made crates for shipment back to the museum in Chicago. In two weeks' time, we can easily collect a couple of tons of cut slabs containing fossils. In 30 years' time, we have built a massive collection of this material in Chicago for use not only by me, but by scientists from all over the world.

— *Lance Grande*

When a fish or other fossil is spotted partially hidden beneath a thin layer of light-colored limestone, it is marked for later collection and preparation, either with a pencil or, as in this image from Ulrichs Quarry, by being partially cut out with a rock saw. Photos © Wendell Ricketts; all rights reserved.

Aerial view of two of the many working Fossil Lake quarries east of Fossil Butte. The wingtip of Mike Stroud's handbuilt, single-engine RV-6 two-seater is visible at bottom. (With many thanks to Mike for his kindness is showing me quarry operations from the air!) Photo © Wendell Ricketts; all rights reserved.

A Monumental Undertaking
Meet the Fossil Butte National Monument's Museum Curator, Arvid Aase

It's hardly a surprise that someone who was once a kid with a rock collection grew up to be a geologist, but Arvid Aase's career path may have slightly exceeded expectations. As a youngster in the Yellowstone Valley of Eastern Montana, Aase (pronounced OH-seh) picked up moss agates, petrified wood, and fossils. Once he reached college, he began taking geology classes, eventually receiving a master's from the University of Kansas. At the suggestion of his friends, the world-famous trilobitologists, the Gunther family, Aase worked his first summer in a Kemmerer, Wyoming-area fish quarry at the age of twenty-two. Eventually, he applied for and was hired as a seasonal interpretive ranger at Fossil Butte National Monument, located about fifteen miles (twenty-four km) west of Kemmerer, Wyoming, one of the National Park Service's most important paleontological museums. Later, he was promoted to museum technician and then museum specialist. Today, Aase is in his seventh year as the Monument's Museum Curator. (He has a secret, though: At heart, he's still a "trilobite guy.")

Although the Fossil Butte area began to be known for its fossils as early as the middle of the nineteenth century, when word of discoveries by missionaries and explorers began to spread, the Fossil Butte National Monument wasn't dedicated until October 1972. Today, its museum collection represents one of the most important interpretive centers in the country for the remarkable Eocene geology and paleontology of Fossil Lake. The museum and its archives currently houses about 49,000 items, including historical photographs of old quarries and long-lost towns (such as the all-but-vanished Fossil,

Wyoming, a stone's throw from Fossil Butte Monument); maps and prints; photographs of fossils and local wildlife; historical documents related to figures such as Lee Craig, one of the earliest full-time fossil quarriers in the U.S., active in the Kemmerer area between 1897 and 1937; and many other items. Oh, and, of course, about 6,000 individual fossils. As technology has changed, photographs and other archival documents now tend to arrive in digital form, and one of the museum's ongoing projects is to create a system for indexing those materials and making them available for study.

Last October, Aase was there to help the Fossil Butte National Monument celebrate its 45th birthday. The fossil-rich sediments that crop out around the visitor center and on the nearby, chalk-colored ridges known as Fossil Butte, however, barely look a day over fifty million. The Monument centers on an extraordinary assemblage of Eocene Epoch animal and plant fossils associated with Fossil Lake—the smallest of the three great lakes that were once present in what are now Wyoming, Utah, and Colorado.

Each year, some 21,000 visitors—more than 80% of them during June, July,

Fossil Butte National Monument Museum Curator, Arvid Aase, left, and Philip Frasier hold a rare fossil bowfin, Cyclurus gurleyi. *Frasier had found the fish in a private Kemmerer quarry and, after partially preparing it, realized it might be an unusual specimen. He donated his find to the museum on the occasion of the National Park Service's 100th Anniversary celebration. NPS photo.*

and August and many still dusting quarry dust off their shoes—come to the Fossil Butte visitor center off Chicken Creek Road, a stretch of highway that crosses a narrow plateau marked by the lichen green of sagebrush and the brown of earth and, during the season, by herds of bright white sheep. There, visitors find one of the best-curated natural-history museums in the U.S. When the "slow" season rolls around, however, the Monument's staff does anything but rest. To the contrary, that's their time to write proposals; plan new exhibits and facility upgrades; revise signage and visitor information; and prepare, catalogue, and study the specimens recovered from the previous quarrying season, among other projects.

In 2017, for example, a mysterious specimen, currently in Lance Grande's lab at the Field Museum in Chicago for

Museum Curator Arvid Aase and Dr. Lance Grande examine an unusual specimen found in American Quarry and brought to the museum in June 2017. Though the fossil is still under study, there are hints that it may represent the first-ever freshwater eel from Fossil Lake.

preparation and study, may be a never-before-discovered freshwater eel. Meanwhile, although just under thirty species of other fish have been identified from the Fossil Butte Formation and are well known, Aase notes that the study of plant and insect species lags behind, despite exciting finds in recent years. These less well-known Fossil Lake insects, Aase says, promise to be "a treasure trove." At the same time, turtles, snakes, bats, alligators, and dog-sized horses and other mammals continue to be found, adding dimension to scientists' understanding of a low, subtropical, freshwater lake basin where sediments, and the fossils they contain, accumulated over a vast period of time.

Fossil fish, though, will perhaps always occupy first place the public mind when it comes to Fossil Lake and

Kemmerer-area quarries. For the 2018 season, for example, Aase, whose "Fishing the Layers of Time" exhibit, a series of interactive displays that connected visitors to the park's extinct aquatic ecosystem, received a prestigious Freeman Tilden Award for excellence in interpretation in 2006, is planning a new exhibit dedicated to growth series of some of Fossil Lake's classic fish, starting with *Knightia* and *Diplomystus*. The display will showcase specimens from quarter-inch hatchlings all the way up to some of the largest adult specimens ever found in the area.

Keeping current on the science is the biggest challenge at the museum, Aase says, which is why he attends the annual meetings of professional associations like the Geological Society of America and the Society of Vertebrate Paleontology, among others, and keeps abreast of the latest scientific literature. Because of the visibility of fossil fish, "our focus at Fossil Butte may seem narrower" with respect to larger museums, Aase adds, but the extent to which the ancient Fossil Lake ecosystem is now known means that he and his interpretive staff "need to know something about insects, and plants, and crayfish, and turtles, and, and, and...." That knowledge is part of what enables Aase and his staff to lead tours, interact with professional paleontologists, and work with master's and PhD students who come to the area for research and whom Aase can connect with cooperative operators where strata or fossils have been exposed that match students' areas of interest.

In fact, Aase works closely with quarry operators, museums, researchers, private collectors, and many others whose interests or professions bring them to Kemmerer—or, as Aase puts it, part of his job is juggling "science, commercial, amateur, and government" interests. That can be a challenge, he says, but it's also "interesting and fun." Local quarry operators show him "all kinds of cool things," including both fossils and geological oddities, and have, over the years, generously donated "hundreds and hundreds of specimens [to Fossil Butte] for science and for exhibit." In return, quarry operators learn more about what's in their quarries and can share that information with their visitors.

The Monument also operates its own research quarry, open to the public, which is located off a trail not far from the museum. Since 1997, the quarry has operated two days a week during the twelve weeks of summer. Visitors can watch how fossils are recovered and, if the weather is cooperative, even participate in digging. To date, some 4,000 fossils have been taken out of the relatively small research quarry exposure and, because the work is purposefully slow and deliberate, Monument workers can brag of achieving as close to 100% recovery as possible.

At the same time, the number of fish and other fossil specimens taken from the Fossil Lake area over the last 160 years is staggering. In his book, *The Lost World of Fossil Lake,* paleontologist Lance Grande reported one worker's estimate that half a million fossil fish had been excavated in Fossil Lake quarries between 1970 and 1994, not counting another million incomplete or damaged fish that were likely thrown away. Grande adds his own calculation that some 200,000 fish are now taken annually from Fossil Lake quarries, and Aase conjectures that something on the order of four million fossils of all kinds have been recovered since the middle of the nineteenth century, even though that only "scratches the surface of what's actually still in the hillsides. Sure, that's a lot of *Knightia*, snails, and flies," he says, "but the biodiversity of species continues to grow as more specimens are recovered," which means that "we haven't plateaued out on the diversity curve yet for certain groups"—and especially not in the case of insects and plants." In fact, as Grande also notes, as sample size grows larger, so does the ability to interpret past biodiversity.

By definition, of course, fossils are a finite resource. As Aase says, "You can't make anymore. Those organisms are extinct and long dead. So you can't get around that limitation, but, in the Fossil Lake area, that limit is rather high. Mother Nature has removed more by erosion in the last several million years that we're ever going to excavate in many lifetimes," he continues. "Right now, considering both the accessible private land and accessible land that hasn't been touched yet," there's enough left to be discovered at Fossil Lake to last at least "two or three more careers."

Amanda Wilson at Lake McDonald, Glacier National Park, Montana. (NPS Photo/Jacob Frank.)

Ranger Amanda Wilson
A Career in the National Parks

I grew up in northern New Jersey in a very outdoorsy family, and I always knew I wanted to follow a profession where I could work outside. I guess I would label myself a geology nerd. Geology was always my favorite subject in school, and I've had a rock collection for as long as I can remember. In college, I majored in Environmental Science and Politics and was lucky enough to get an internship at Glacier National Park in northwest Montana. My life hasn't been the same since!

After reading a book called *Interpreting Our Heritage* by Freeman Tilden in preparation for that internship, I knew that working with the National Park Service was the place for me. When I finished college, I moved to Montana and continued to work at Glacier for the next five years. Next, I got a permanent job with the National Park Service (NPS) in Fairbanks, Alaska, working for Gates of the Arctic National Park and Preserve/Yukon Charley National Preserve. After a few other stops along the way, I came to work at Fossil Butte National Monument.

At Fossil Butte, my official title was Supervisory Park Ranger-Interpretation, which basically means helping visitors create meaningful connections between themselves and the resources of the NPS. The moment when you see that "ah ha!" look on someone's face is the most rewarding thing you can hope to do.

Not long ago, I moved to Dinosaur National Monument where I'm a Park Guide. At Fossil Butte my favorite fossil was the cast of *Onychonycteris finneyi*. It's the one of the earliest known fossil bats and doesn't appear to have developed echolocation. I think it is a beautiful, delicately preserved fossil with an amazing story. Here, it's harder to pick an individual favorite fossil, but I love working in the Quarry Exhibit Hall because of the incredible reactions people have when they see the wall of dinosaur fossils in person.

There's no such thing as a typical day in my job, which is why working for the NPS is so much fun! It's great to share excitement like that with people of all ages and leave them with a greater appreciation of the amazing places the NPS helps to protect.

Counter-clockwise from top: 1. *Fossil Butte is capped by limestone deposited by ancient Fossil Lake, part of the famous Green River Formation. Sagebrush steppe vegetation dominates the surrounding landscape. Photo by Tyra Olstad; © National Park Service. 2. Fossil Butte National Monument map, showing hiking trails, visitor center, and the research quarry, open to visitors twice a week during the summer. 3. The cover of the forty-four-page proposal for the creation of the Fossil Butte National Monument (https://www.nps.gov/parkhistory/online_books/fobu/fobu_proposed.pdf). Though the proposal was submitted to the Department of the Interior in September 1964, Fossil Butte National Monument was not established until almost exactly eight years later.*

Birds, Beasts, Blossoms, and Bugs:
Specimens from the Extraordinary Collections at Fossil Butte

Three specimens from the Fossil Butte National Monument's archival collections. Above left: A water-strider-like insect.
Right : a species of beetle. Below: A well-preserved decapod crustacean.

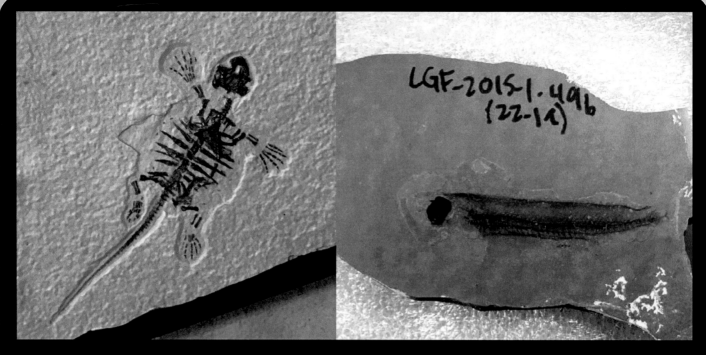

Above left: *A cast of a juvenile specimen of* Chesternon undatum, *a member of an extinct family of turtles, about 6" long; the original is in a private collection.* Right: *One of the Angelo Member's most unusual fossils, "ghost fish" are found without bones, though they sometimes preserve organic material such as skin and eyes. Studies are underway to determine what taphonomic conditions, including possibly high pH and alkalinity at the end of Fossil Lake's life, produced this unique mode of preservation.* Below: *A cast of the holotype of* Pseudocrypturus cercanaxius, *a relative of such modern birds as ostriches, collected from Fossil Lake. The original resides at the Smithsonian.*

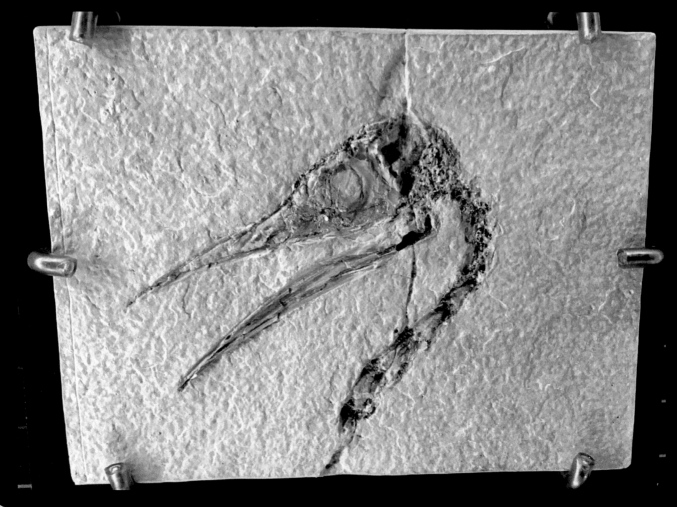

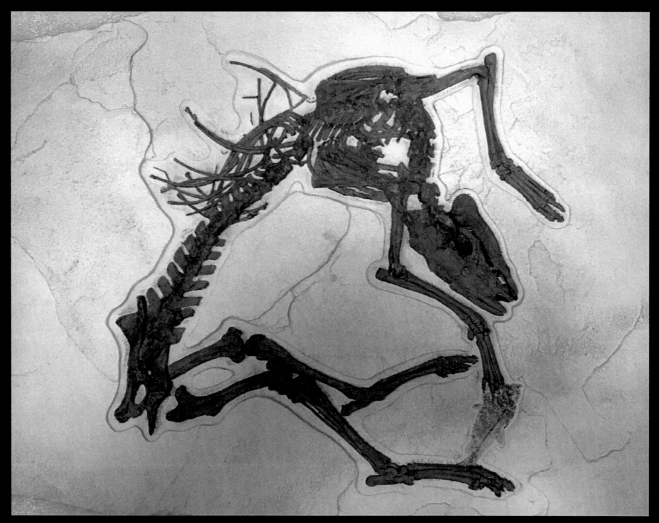

Above: *A cast of one of two extraordinary horses found at Fossil Lake.* Below left: Comptonia *sp., a species of sweet fern.* Right: *Unidentified flower from the museum's extensive collection of plant materials. Fossilized plants are more difficult to identify because their parts often become separated before they are preserved. It may never be possible to connect this flower to the plant that produced it.*

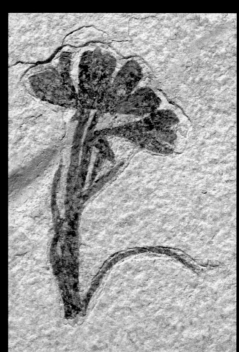

New Species or Natural Variation?

A favorite find for collectors in the Fossil Butte Formation are specimens of *Priscacara*, an extinct genus of perch. One reason for *Priscacara*'s popularity is that well-prepared specimens sport a row of formidable-looking dorsal spines and, usually, three no less impressive anal spines.

Over the years, however, a handful of apparent *P. serrata* have been found with four anal spines rather than three (see red arrow, at right). The Field Museum's Dr. Lance Grande has been tracking the phenomenon, noting that the four-spined variety might represent a new species but is perhaps more likely simply a natural variation (think six-toed cats). Other than the extra spine, Grande says, "I can't see anything that ties the [four-spine fish] together, but I'm continuing to look at that."

As more and more fossils are collected, and sample sizes grow, naturally-occuring population variations are constantly being clarified. Grande, for example, estimates in *Lost World of Fossil Lake* that 8,000-plus *P. serrata* were taken from area quarries between 1870 and 2010 (see his Table 1, p. 177), but anecdotal evidence suggests that four-anal-spined specimens may number less than a dozen.

Shown here are two four-spined specimens: *Above and inset*—From the Robert Bowen collection; prepped and photographed by Robert Bowen, Wyoming Fossils. *Below left*—A four-spined, 6-3/8" specimen from the 18-inch layer. Adam Lindgren Quarry; prepped by Adam Lindgren. Photo © Katie Lindgren, Ancient Lake Fossils Inc. *Bottom right*: A *P. serrata* with the more common three anal spines. (NPS photo.)

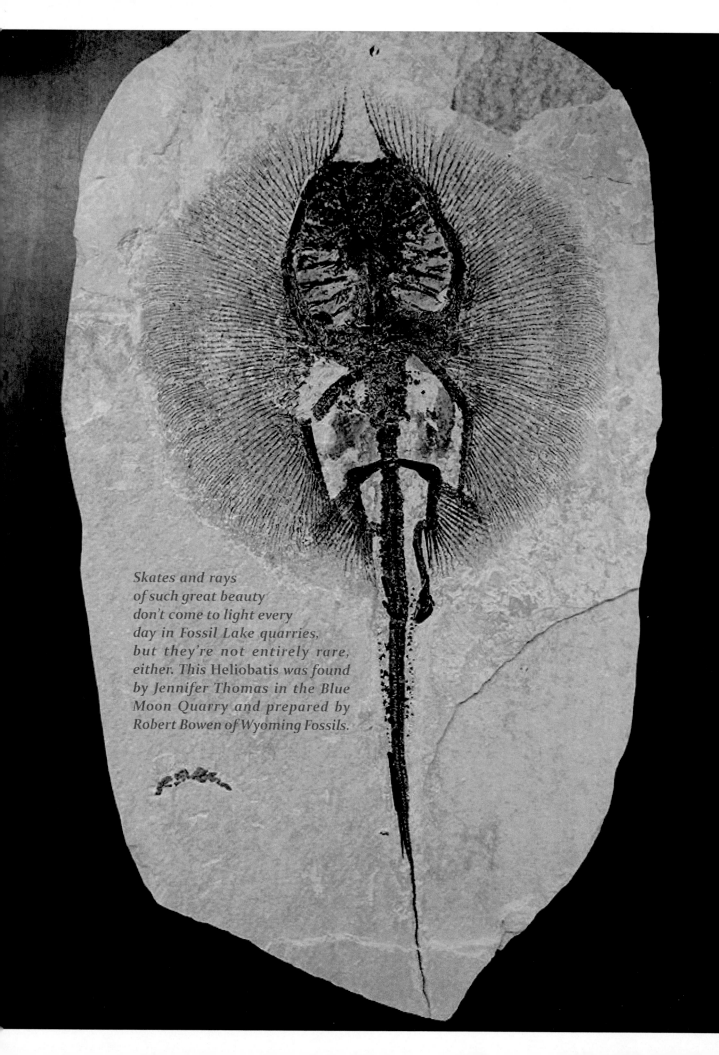

Skates and rays of such great beauty don't come to light every day in Fossil Lake quarries, but they're not entirely rare, either. This Heliobatis was found by Jennifer Thomas in the Blue Moon Quarry and prepared by Robert Bowen of Wyoming Fossils.

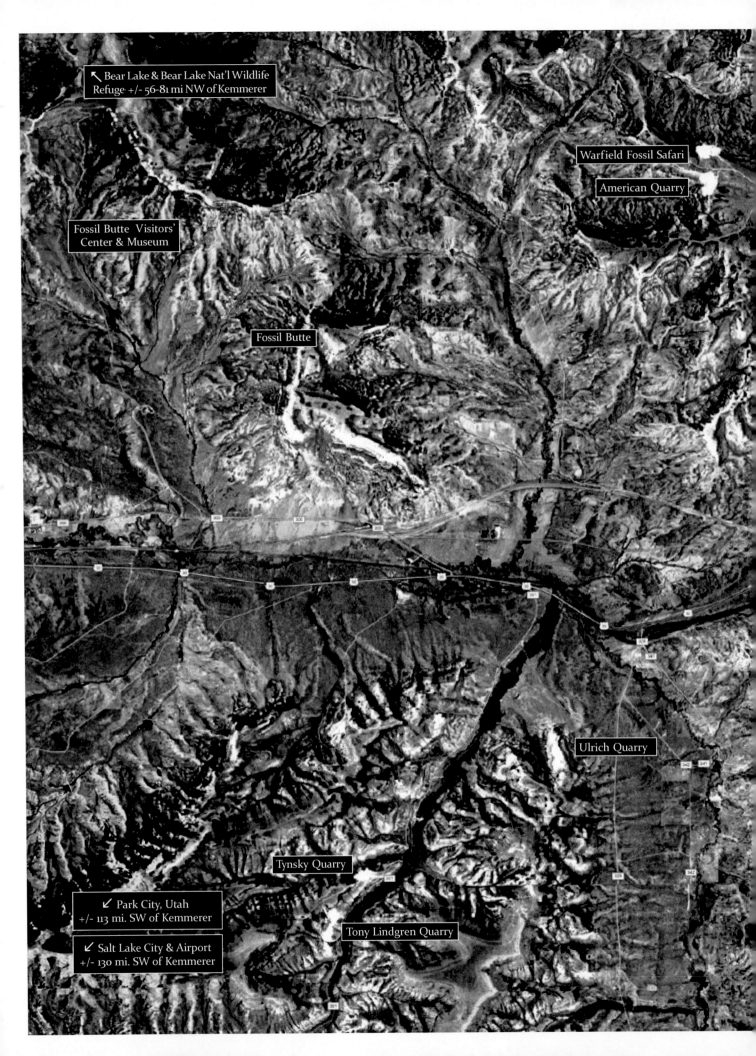

Bear Lake & Bear Lake Nat'l Wildlife Refuge +/- 56-81 mi NW of Kemmerer

Warfield Fossil Safari

American Quarry

Fossil Butte Visitors' Center & Museum

Fossil Butte

Ulrich Quarry

Tynsky Quarry

Park City, Utah +/- 113 mi. SW of Kemmerer

Tony Lindgren Quarry

Salt Lake City & Airport +/- 130 mi. SW of Kemmerer

↑ Grand Teton Nat'l Park
+/- 170 mi. N of Kemmerer

↗ Wyoming Dinosaur Center
+/- 227 mi. NE of Kemmerer

↖ Cokeville Meadows Nat'l Wildlife
Refuge, +/- 50 mi NW of Kemmerer

→ Pilot Butte Wild Horse Scenic
Loop, +/- 90 mi E of Kemmerer

↗ White Mountain Petroglyphs &
Killpecker Sand Dunes
+/- 120 mi. NE of Kemmerer

2" = approx. 1.8 miles

Kemmerer
Municipal Airport

Blue Moon Quarry

Westmoreland Kemmerer
Coal Mine

Kemmerer

Diamondville

→ Seedskadee Nat'l Wildlife Refuge
+/- 50 mi E of Kemmerer

↗ Casper-Natrona Int'l Airport
+/- 300 mi. NE of Kemmerer

↓ Uinta-Wasatch-Cache Nat'l Forest,
+/- 80 mi. S of Kemmerer

↘ Flaming Gorge Nat'l Rec Area
+/- 90 mi. SE of Kemmerer

↘ Dinosaur Nat'l Monument
+/- 170 mi. SE of Kemmerer

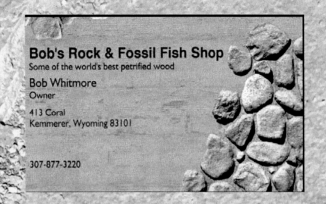

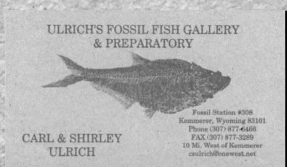

Rock & Fossil Shops

Fossils, Minerals, Wood, Books, Supplies ... and more!

Bob's Rock & Fossil Fish Shop
413 Coral Street
Kemmerer, WY 83101
307.877.3220

Fossil Shack
American Fossil Quarry
https://www.fossilshack.com
(online only)

Tynsky's Fossil Fish
716 J.C. Penney Drive
Kemmerer, WY 83101
www.tynskysfossilfish.com
jetynsky@hotmail.com
307. 877.6885

Ulrich's Fossil Fish Gallery
4400 County Road 300
Kemmerer, WY 83101
www.ulrichsfossilgallery.com
csulrich@onewest.net
307. 877.6466

Wyoming Fossils & Minerals
921 Pine Avenue
Kemmerer, WY 83101
www.wyomingfossils.com
robert@wyomingfossils.com
254.223.3204

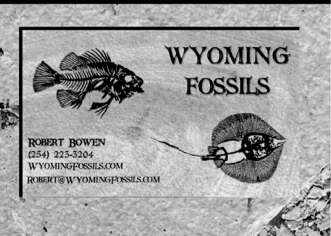

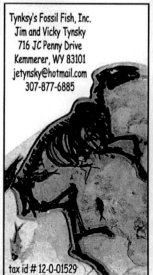

Dig-Your-Own Quarries

Blue Moon Quarry
http://promiselandfossils.com
307.877.3641
By appointment only

Tynsky Quarry
www.tynskysfossilfish.com
jetynsky@hotmail.com
307. 877-6885

Warfield Fossil Quarries
http://www.fossilsafari.com
warfosq@silverstar.com

Discounts for Fossil News Readers!

American Fossil Quarry
http://www.fishdig.com
801.836.7269
**Mention code
FOSNEWS10DISC when
booking for 10% off dig fees!**

Ulrich Quarry
www.ulrichsfossilgallery.com
csulrich@onewest.net
307. 877-6466
**Mention code FOSNEWS when
booking for $5 off dig fees!**

NB: Quarries vary widely in fees, hours,
the number and kind of specimens visitors are allowed to keep, and other rules
and procedures. Always check before you
go. Several private quarries also operate
in the area and may sometimes accom-
modate individuals or groups. Ask at local
rock shops.

Above: *Ulrich Quarry workers Cole Jackman and
Logan Marable inspect the dig surface before
guests arrive. Photo © Wendell Ricketts; all rights
reserved. Below: A spectacular feather from the
Tynksy Quarry. Skyler Phelps Collection. Photo
© Lynn Fischbeck ; used by permission.*

Lodging In & Around Kemmerer

Antler Motel
419 Coral Street, Kemmerer
307-877-4461

Best Western Fossil Country Inn
760 Highway 189/30, Kemmerer
307-877-3388
www.bestwestern.com

Dee's Motel
1325 Central Avenue, Kemmerer
307-877-3288

Fairview Motel
61 US Highway 30, Diamondville
307-877-3938
www.fairview-kemmerer.com

Fossil Butte Motel
1424 Central Avenue, Kemmerer
307-877-3996

Frontier Suites
113 Wyoming Highway 233,
Kemmerer
307-877-3377

Super 8
3 US Highway 30 189, Diamondville
307-877-6901
www.wyndhamhotels.com

Cowboy Joe RV Park
97 Sublet, Diamondville
307-877-6693

Foothills Mobile Home & RV Park
310 US 189, Kemmerer
307-877-6634

Ham's Fork Grill & RV Park
307 Highway 189 N, Kemmerer
307-877-8848

Riverside RV Park
216 Spinel, Kemmerer
307-877-3416

City of Kemmerer Tent Campground
Highway 233 near Kemmerer City Hall. Tents only; no reservations.
307-828-2360

Weeping Rock Campground
Highway 372 (about 30 miles east of Kemmerer)
GPS: 42.02075, -110.04957
307-828-4500

Reserve early where possible. Summer is high season in Fossil Basin!

Eats & Entertainment

Restaurants/Diners

Bootleggers
817 S. Main Street, Kemmerer
307-828-3067

Caribou Café
1012 Pine Avenue, Kemmerer
307-800-8888

El Jalisciense
1433 Central Avenue, Kemmerer
307-877-2948

Ham's Fork Grill
307 Highway 189 N, Kemmerer
307-877-8848

Jailhouse Java Joint
700 Cedar Avenue, Kemmerer
(307) 828-9150

Luigi's
807 Susie Avenue, Diamondville
307-877-6221

Mandarin Garden
801 S. Main Street, Kemmerer
307-877-3556

Place on Pine
919 Pine Avenue, Kemmerer
307-877-2982

Sage Lanes & Grill
918 Sage Avenue, Kemmerer
307-877-3805

Scroungy Moose Pizza
179 Wyoming Highway 233, Kemmerer
307-877-4233

Fast Food
Arctic Circle (04 US-30, Diamondville),
307-877-3557; **Pizza Hut** (335 Highway 30-
189, Diamondville), 307-877-1111
Subway (189 US-30, Diamondville), 307-
877-1244; **Taco Time** (1121 Coral Avenue,
Kemmerer), 307-877-3357

Entertainment/Recreation

Fossil Country Museum
400 Pine Avenue, Kemmerer
307-877-6551

Fossil Island Golf Club
105 Wyoming Highway 233
307-877-6954

J C Penney "Mother Store"
722 J C Penney Drive, Kemmerer

Kemmerer Outdoor Pool
1100 Post Place
307-828-2365

Kemmerer Recreation Center
1776 Del Rio
307-828-2365

Sage Lanes & Grill
918 Sage Avenue, Kemmerer
307-877-3805

Victory Theatre
720 JC Penney Drive, Kemmerer
307-877-6684

Westmoreland Kemmerer Coal Mine
6520 County Rd 304
Tours by apppointment only. Contact
the mine office at (307) 828-2200

Seasonal Events

Fossil Fest - Kemmerer
www.fossilfest.org
June 29-30, 2018

Kemmerer Little Buckaroo Rodeo
www.littlebuckaroorodeo.com
Mid-July

Lincoln County Fair and Rodeo
Afton, WY, 307-885-9838
www.lincolncountyfair.info
August 4-11, 2018

Oyster Ridge Music Festival
Diamondville, 307-877-6958
Oysterridgemusicfestival.com
Late July

The Oyster Ridge Music Festival
Oyster·grass
Wyoming's Largest FREE Music Festival
Downtown Kemmerer at The Historic Triangle Park

FOSSILFEST
JUNE 29-30, 2018

Downtown Kemmerer, Wyoming
www.fossilfest.org

Kemmerer Is Coal Country
The "Other" Fossiils of Fossil Basin

Slabs of beautifully preserved fish and other Eocene lake creatures may be the most famous of Kemmerer, Wyoming's fossils, but there's another relict of past eons that is both older still and the real reason the town exists at all: coal.

Explorer John C. Fremont, whom history also remembers as the first presidential candidate of the anti-slavery Republican Party in 1856, discovered coal in the Kemmerer area during an expedition in 1843, and the Union Pacific Coal Company opened the first underground Kemmerer coal mine in 1881. Some sixteen years later, Patrick J. Quealy, vice-president of the Kemmerer Coal Company, founded Kemmerer as an "independent town," and, by 1950, the Kemmerer operation was the world's largest open pit coal mine. In the years between then and 2011, the mine is estimated to have yielded 169,831,453 tons of coal.

Founded in Pennsylvania in 1854, the Westmoreland Coal Company acquired the Kemmerer mine in 2012. Today, the mine, classified a "truck and shovel" surface-mine operation (vs. underground or strip-mining), is a 13,400-acre complex that employs about 300 and produces nearly five million tons of coal each year from three active areas. A massive overland conveyor system carries coal directly to the adjacent Naughton Power Station, and trains eighty-cars or more long snake away from the mine, ferrying coal to more distant destinations.

Depending upon mining operations and availability of personnel, tours of the mine can be arranged on an appointment-only basis. Contact the Westmoreland-Kemmerer Coal Mine office at 307.828.2200.

Top: *In the distance, an excavator works a coal seam. Note the steep "dip" or angle of the darker seam. Photo © Wendell Ricketts; all rights reserved.* Center: *A close-up of a lump of "raw" coal from the mine. Photo © Lydia Defranchi-Nelson; used by permission.* Bottom: *Westmoreland-Kemmerer operates seventeen 240-ton haul trucks. Here, an employee is dwarfed by one of the truck's giant tires. Photo © Wendell Ricketts; all rights reserved.*

A "Fossil" Presence

Lance Grande on the Seven-Decade Dynasty of the Ulrich Clan

The Ulrich family is probably the best known of the commercial Kemmerer-area quarriers today. Carl and Shirley Ulrich began working the FBM in 1947 around the vicinity of Fossil Butte and eventually moved to land leased from the state of Wyoming, where their work crews still quarry today. My own first experience digging in the FBM began with a week on the Ulrich commercial quarry many years before I had finished graduate school and become a professional paleontologist. Although I had to buy each fish that I found, I learned a few early tricks of the quarrying trade from Carl and his work crews. Their years of experience working the FBM rock had taught them techniques that they freely relayed to me, many of which I still use today with my own quarry crews from the Field Museum.

Carl Ulrich, born in 1925, started working in the 1940s as an underground coal miner south of Diamondville and as a part-time card dealer in the casinos of Kemmerer and Jackson, Wyoming. As a child he had dug for fossils on Fossil Butte with David Haddenham. Shirley Ulrich was the daughter of parents who worked for the coal mine in the days when the mine held its workers in virtual servitude, and she had no desire to follow in their footsteps. In the late 1940s, the Ulrichs started looking for FBM fossils as a hobby but managed to sell a few pieces, which eventually convinced them to [try their hands] at the commercial fossil business. Things started slowly but eventually blossomed into an extremely successful enterprise

Above: *Examining an enormous palm frond found in the Ulrichs' quarry around 2000. Photo © Shirley Ulrich; used by permission.* Below: *Ulrich Quarry employee Tanner Housley uses a rock saw to remove a slab containing a fossil from the exposed quarry floor. © Ulrich Fossil Gallery; used by permission.*

AAPS, The Association of Applied Paleontological Sciences was organized in 1978 to create a professional association of commercial fossil dealers, collectors, enthusiasts, and academic paleontologists for the purpose of promoting ethical collecting practices and cooperative liaisons with researchers, instructors, curators and exhibit managers in the paleontological academic and museum community.

Please Join Us

- Keep current on International Fossil Laws
- Help us fight unreasonable state "Fossil Ivory" bans
- Learn About new "Casual Collecting" regulations
- Get invitations to all AAPS meetings, dinners, and events
- Recieve monthly Newsletters and special notices
- Pick up the Annual Tucson Guide to Dealers & Events

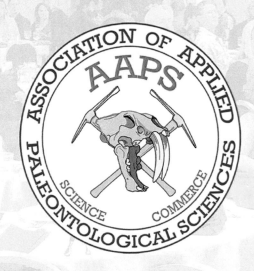

Membership Application - www.AAPS.net/membership.pdf

SPECIAL FOR THE SUBCRIBERS OF

FOSSIL NEWS MAGAZINE

JOIN AAPS BEFORE THE END OF 2017

AND YOUR DUES WILL INCLUDE 2018

"ALL MEMBERSHIP CATEGORIES"

that still thrives today. The Ulrichs were awarded some of the very first of the commercial fossil quarrying permits from the state of Wyoming in the late 1960s, and they have been working the same FBM quarry for decades. Through their permit, they are allowed to keep and sell most of the fossils that they find, but as with all the state commercial quarries, they are required to turn some of the rarer species of vertebrate fossils over to the Wyoming Geological Survey (e.g., birds, bats, turtles, amphibians, crocodilians, and mammals).

The Ulrichs were among the first of the twentieth-century commercial quarriers to take special care and use modern tools in the preparation of many of their fossils, particularly the rarer pieces. They were strong advocates of protecting federal lands from commercial exploitation and helped campaign for the creation of a national park to preserve significant portions of the FBM. In 1972, with the creation of Fossil Butte National Monument, the park became a reality. For the Ulrichs and the other legal commercial quarriers, this preserve served a dual purpose. First, it showed altruistic foresight in preserving a part of this national heritage for future generations. Second, it eliminated a lot of potential competition and uncontrolled outside exploitation. Everyone benefited from the initiative in the end.

The Ulrichs' business profile and political recognition grew through the late twentieth century. In 1960, Presi-

A portrait of Carl Ulrich in his prep lab by Rock Springs, Wyoming-based artist, Glenn Taucher, a long-time family friend. Based on a photo taken about thirty years ago, the portrait hangs in the Ulrichs' living room.

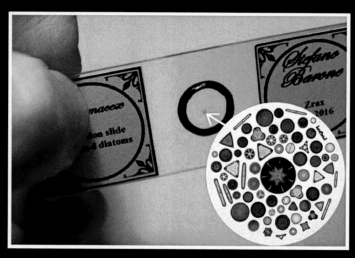
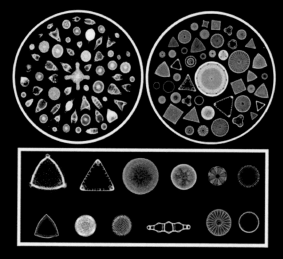

Carl Ulrich with a gar taken from the Ulrich Quarry in the early 1960s. Because the combined duties of a commercial quarrier and gallery owner were so time-consuming, Carl took nearly a decade to finish prepping the specimen. Photo © Shirley Ulrich; used by permission.

dent Eisenhower purchased a large *Diplomystus dentatus* from Carl Ulrich to present as a gift to Japan's Emperor Hirohito from the American people. During the George H. W. Bush presidency, Secretary of State Jim Baker would occasionally buy FBM fossils from the Ulrichs to present to foreign officials. Carl and Shirley were also friends with Casper, Wyoming, resident Dick Cheney before he became vice president of the United States, and they grew up with early Kemmerer resident Edgar Herschler, who later served as governor of Wyoming from 1975 to 1987.

Carl and Shirley built a very successful business out of their FBM fossil operations, and their pieces are in museums and private collections all over the world. In 1979 they moved from the town of Kemmerer to the defunct town of Fossil, where they built a large house at the base of Fossil Butte just outside the park on the road to the Fossil Butte National Monument visitor center. From this beautiful estate and prime location, huge windows look out on the main butte of the monument, and the famous Twin Creek runs just outside their back door. (Paleontologist E. D. Cope used "Twin

Creek" as his name for the Fossil Butte localities.) The Ulrichs also have a fossil-preparation facility and sales floor located in the building that is visited by many tourists each day. With the emigration of the Ulrichs to Fossil, the population was once again on the rise, boosted to a grand total of five residents.

— *Lance Grande*

Discovering & Photographing Ostracods in Eocene Green River "*Turritella* Agate"

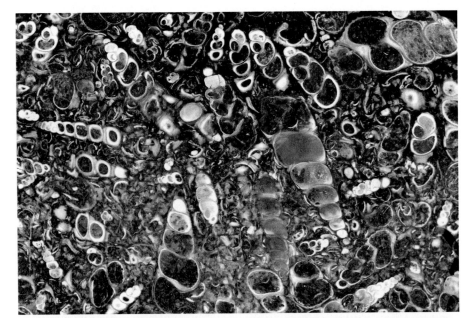

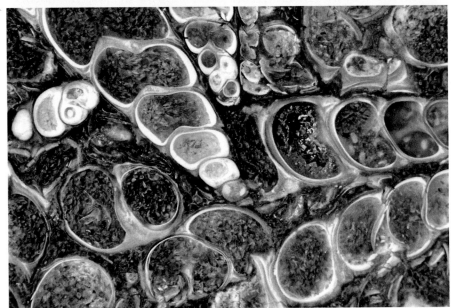

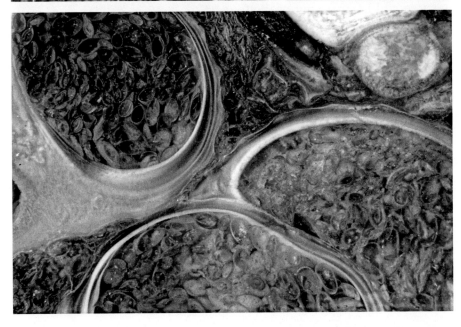

One pleasure of life in "retirement" is being able to contribute to worthy causes, perhaps to advance knowledge and awareness. Having been a photographer since 1960, I have some proficiency in that medium. My interest in geology and paleontology from early childhood made the North America Research Group (NARG) a natural place to offer my services.

NARG members do many constructive things, from "search and rescue" of fossils to prepping them, to holding regular events meant to interest and educate the public in paleontology. We attend rock-and-mineral shows regularly with elaborate display cases of fossils that serve as show-and tell-tables staffed by experts. They are a natural place for me to set up demonstrations of stacked-focus photography, where people can watch on a monitor as I make multiple exposures at incremental focus ranges, then stack them together into one sharp image.

To do this, I put together a transportable assembly consisting of an old photo darkroom enlarger chassis with the enlarger head removed and a camera mount installed. On that, I installed StackShot computer-controlled microfocusing rail mounts and a modern digital camera on a forty-five-year-old bellows, with an assortment of lenses adapted for microphotography.

Using the enlarger gave me control of vertical movement, and having the subject held down by gravity was much easier than trying to prop or clamp irregularly shaped rocks. To facilitate leveling the subject, I used a deli salad container half-full of aquarium sand. When a subject needs to be backlit, I put aluminum foil over the sand to reflect light

through the specimen, then put the object on the transparent lid that came with the salad.

The camera, either a Nikon D800e or Olympus OM-D E-M5 MkII, is connected to a computer through a USB connection. I do not look through the camera itself. Rather, I run everything through the computer. All of this sits on a cart, so I can haul it to an event in my car, put it together in the parking lot, roll it in, and be at work within minutes.

The images included here show a "discovery" I made at a 2015 rock and mineral show. Someone asked me to shoot a slab of what is commonly but erroneously called "*Turritella* Agate." "*Turritella* Agate" is the popular name for a brown, translucent, fossiliferous agate fairly common in the Eocene Green River Formation of southern Wyoming, but the elongated, tall-spiraled shells are actually freshwater gastropods, *Elimia tenera*. (*Turritella* were and are exclusively marine.) The rock in which these shells are found ranges varies from soft sandstone to dense chalcedony (agate is a variety of chalcedony).

In any case, I made the photos as requested. The mesmerizing shapes of those crosscut deep spiral shells was enticing, but I was using a sharp lens and thought there might be more, in closer. Under greater magnification, the dark gray matrix proved to be full of ostracods, many of which photographed in brilliant colors. Using some of my best lenses at high magnification, textures on the ostracod carapaces became obvious, yet another universe right in front of us.

— *Joe Cantrell*

Preceding pages: Osctracods in association with sectioned specimens of the freshwater gastropod, Elimia tenera, *from the Green River "*Turritella Agate.*" All photographs © Joe Cantrell; used by permission.*

Proud supporter of the Gary S. Morgan Student Research Award and National Fossil Day™

floridapaleosociety.com

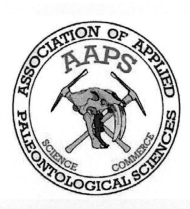

American Fossil: The Education Quarry

There's no shortage of Kemmerer-area quarries for visitors who want to split rock to find fish and other Eocene Green River fossils, but for teachers in the natural sciences, there's only one that deserves to be called "the Education Quarry": Seth Sorensen, Patrick Hogle, and Jeff Peterson's American Fossil.

Located in an area of Fossil Lake that has been quarried steadily for more than a century, the American Fossil

ing Extinct 'Lords of the Night' in the Eocene Quarries of Wyoming's Green River Formation ... and Beyond," *Fossil News*, Spring 2016.)

But that wasn't the only impressive find from the American Fossil site. One of only two known three-toed horses from Fossil Lake was found there, and last season, Sorensen notes, several crocodiles, three turtles (all found in one day), and yet another possible bat species

A cloudless, brilliant blue sky extends over the dig site at American Fossil Quarry, Summer 2017. Photo © Wendell Ricketts; all rights reserved.

site is sometimes still referred to by such older names as Thompson Ranch and the South Dempsey Quarry, and it was worked for many years by Bonnie and Bob Finney. Bonnie's 2008 discovery there of a primitive, apparently non-echolocating bat rewrote the history of bat evolution and provided evidence for the "flight-first" hypothesis—in other words, the proposition that bats developed the ability to fly before they developed echolocation. The extraordinary find was eventually named *Onychonycteris finneyi*, or "Finney's clawed bat," in honor of Bonnie Finney, who passed away in 2013. (See "Blame it on the Bats! Track-

were recovered. One find, perhaps more interesting to paleontologists than to private collectors, was a trace fossil, Sorensen recounts: "We uncovered the imprints of the hands, belly, and tail of a crocodile where it had lain on the bottom of lake."

Last summer, one young visitor, a ten-year-old boy, found a small bird in a piece of shale, a specimen he donated to Yale's Peabody Museum. In fact, though American Fossil is the only Kemmerer quarry—and one of the only commercial fossil sites in the United States—to allow visitors to keep anything they find, their clients almost always donate rare or unusual fossils to science. "We typically recommend that they do that," Sorensen says, "and very occasionally we'll even offer to buy a specimen so we can donate it. That way, something valuable ends up available for study. But 'keep what you find' is just our basic philosophy. As a fossil hunter and collector myself, I like to be able to keep the fossils I find. And everyone else does, too, and if they find something great, we want them to be able to say, 'Hey, look what I found.'"

The fossils aren't what make the quarry unique, though. Rather, it's Sorensen's and his partners' dedication to making their slice of Fossil Lake into an open-air laboratory for teachers. Each June, July, and August, American Fossil hosts a series of "Teacher Day Camps" for educators. Groups of about twenty-five teachers at a time pay a nominal fee for a "behind the scenes" tour of the museum at Fossil Butte National Monument, a hot lunch under the big, blue sky at the quarry, and a chance to find their own fossils at the quarry. At cutting stations along the edge of the parking area, teachers can

L-R: *Seth Sorensen, Patrick Hogle, Brooke Hogle at American Fossil. Photo © Rachelle Sorensen; used by permission.*

have their finds trimmed for transport and get a basic lesson in how to prep fossils, and there's no limit to how many boxes of "rejects" or broken specimens teachers can take back to their classrooms for students' use. They also go home with packets of useful and well-conceived instructional materials, including lesson plans and suggestions for activities. Past Teacher Day Camps have attracted educators from Kindergarten to college

and everything in between, and the enthusiasm at the day camps is palpable.

For Sorensen and Hogle, who are both educators by profession (they became friends while teaching at an alternative high school), the decision to operate an "education quarry" alongside their public, dig-your-own quarry was a natural offshoot of their experience as teachers. Sorensen had also been collecting fossils since he was a youngster ("I used to frustrate my mom because I'd fill my drawers with rocks and fossils instead of clothes," he says, "and I probably burned out two or three washing machines because my pockets were always full of rocks and fossils and I'd forget them in the wash"), but Hogle, a wildlife biologist, wasn't yet infected with the fossil bug when they first met.

Sorensen, a statistician by training, was subleasing dig sites from other Kemmerer quarry operators at the time, and he kept inviting Hogle to collect fossils with him. "It took a few months to convince him to come out here," Sorensen recalls," but as soon as he did, he said, 'We've got to have our own quarry.' It all kind of blossomed from there."

Both men knew there wasn't a lot of money in education, Sorensen says, and "we thought this could be a way to give back a little bit, to give teachers an authentic paleontology experience where they're out in the field digging but still treat them like professionals—just give them a good experience that will add to what they're doing in the classroom and hopefully kindle excitement in their students."

Meanwhile, Sorensen seems to be having about as much fun as it's legal to have in Wyoming. Eternally a "math guy," he's been keeping detailed data on the quarry for years, and he now has enough information to hypothesize that the American Fossil site may not represent a deep-lake environment, as has previously been thought, but was rather "much nearer the eastern shore than current maps suggest"—perhaps even with "some kind of a river or stream that flowed NE to SW and emptied into the lake." His evidence includes the orientations of the fossil fish found in the quarry; the presence of small musk turtles, which typically live in streams or ponds; the discovery of the primitive three-toed horse currently known as *Protorohippus*, which may have been washed into the lake; and even the odd find of a pair of large, completely compressed tree trunks. Sorensen explains, "There were mass deposits of little fish fry on the southwest side of those trunks. So the trees acted to create a barrier, and those small fish, when they died, flowed over and were trapped in water circulating behind."

Sorensen pauses. "Well, I guess that may not sound exciting to most people," he laughs, "but to us it felt pretty significant."

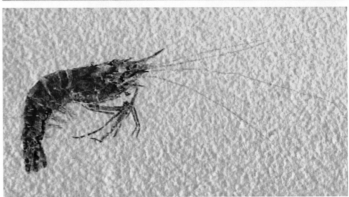

A few spectacular specimens from the American Fossil quarry. Above: Phareodus, *one of Fossil Lake's classic, beautiful fish. Below that, a freshwater shrimp with delicate antennae preserved. Both photos © American Fossil. Bottom left:* Onychonycteris finneyi, *the bat discovered by Bonnie Finney at the site of what is now American Fossil and named after her in 2008. Photo licensed under the Creative Commons Attribution-Share Alike 4.0 International license.*

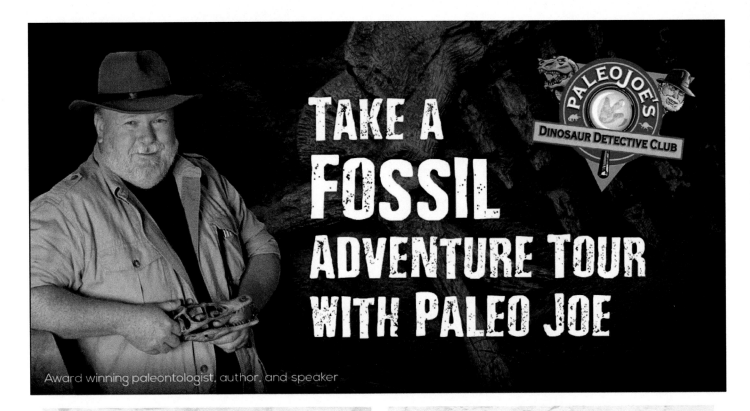

TAKE A FOSSIL ADVENTURE TOUR WITH PALEO JOE

Award winning paleontologist, author, and speaker

PALEO JOE'S DINOSAUR DETECTIVE CLUB

WYOMING'S FOSSILS & DINOSAUR TREASURES

Kemmerer & Thermopolis, WY

Package prices starting at

$799 Adult
(double occupancy)

$449 Children

Inclusions

- One night's accommodations in Evanston
- One night's accommodations in Riverton
- Breakfast at each hotel
- Two boxed lunches
- Two dinners
- Evening introduction and presentation with Paleo Joe
- Two full days of digging with Paleo Joe
- Admission to Fossil Safari
- Admission to Wyoming Dinosaur Center
- You GET TO KEEP some of the Treasures! (fish fossils only)

DIGGING IN MICHIGAN'S ANCIENT SEA

Alpena, Michigan

Package prices starting at

$549 Adult
(double occupancy)

$279 Children

Inclusions

- Two nights' accommodations at Thunder Bay Resort
- Two breakfasts at the resort
- Two boxed lunches
- One five-course dinner including wine pairing at Thunder Bay Resort
- Carriage and Elk ride
- One full day of digging with Paleo Joe
- Evening introduction and presentation by Paleo Joe
- Shipwreck glass-bottom cruise
- Admission to Thunder Bay National Marine Sanctuary - including Science on the Sphere
- You GET TO KEEP all the fossils you find!

CALL 313.575.8888 EXT. 185 OR 122 TO LEARN MORE!

EDUCATIONAL TOURS
BY CORPORATE TRAVEL

Denver Coliseum Show

September 8 – 16, 2018

AMERICA'S LARGEST SHOW

5 Miles of Tables | 500 Dealers | 50,000 Visitors

Come browse 500 wholesale & retail dealers on both levels of the Coliseum, all three levels of the adjacent National Western Complex, plus a plethora of tents behind both historic buildings. It's all here: fossils, minerals, meteorites, gemstones, jewelry, rough, equipment, supplies, and more. We are Denver's only 9-day, weekend-to-weekend show and the nation's single largest show for fossils. Free Parking and Free Entry.

More information at **www.Denver.Show**

Joe Budd Photo.
Arkenstone aquamarine specimens.

A Monitor Lizard from Green River
The Find of a Lifetime

The fifty-million-year-old shale layers that make up the world-renowned Green River Formation in southwestern Wyoming once lay at the bottom of a large inland lake. Despite the arid environs that currently characterize this rather desolate corner of the American landscape, back in the Eocene Epoch this entire area was part of a subtropical zone rich with an abundance of fauna and flora, including everything from primitive flying bats to swaying palm trees.

It was the ancient lake system itself, however, that provided the area with its most notable inhabitants—a diverse array of fish species, including fresh water perch, gar, and herring whose fossilized remains can today can be found throughout these layers, often in prodigious numbers. Indeed, ever since its discovery as one of the world's richest paleontological repositories back in the mid-nineteenth century, the Green River Formation has produced fossil fish by the tens of thousands, each specimen sandwiched between layers of easily split shale. Over the years, commercial diggers have literally turned mountains into molehills in their quest for the wonderfully preserved examples that emerge from the formation's most famed horizon, the "18-Inch Layer." There, the oil-rich shale has preserved the fossils in a dark chocolate brown, which contrasts dramatically against the mottled tan matrix.

While its beautiful and scientifically significant fish fossils have rightfully garnered this formation international renown, the remains of even more exotic creatures, including stingrays, birds, turtles, and alligators, can also occasionally be found within these rocks—often preserved in exquisite detail with virtually every fin, claw, and vertebra now majestically exhibited in stone. Despite the decades of work that have already gone into the digging, preparation, and study of the diverse fossil material that has emerged from the Green River Formation, however, something sometimes still pops up in these layers that not only surprises ... but amazes!

In 2013, the second complete Eocene-age horse ever found was unearthed in the South Dempsey Quarry (now American Quarry). Astonishingly, though, only a few weeks after that headline-generating discovery was made, a perhaps even more mind-blowing find emerged from these hallowed rocks ... a complete monitor lizard! With its rows of fang-like teeth, de-

Saniwa ensidens, *the Green River Formation monitor lizard from Tony Lindgren's quarry. Photo © Tony Lindgren; used by permission.*

tailed limbs, and long sinuous tail, this creature stands as one of the most impressive fossils ever to come out of this legendary location.

"This is the largest fossil lizard ever found in the Green River Formation," says Anthony "Tony" Lindgren, who both discovered and prepared the specimen. His family has been involved in the exploration of the formation's rich layers for more than three decades, and Lindgren himself has been digging fossils since he was 16.

This amazing fossil represents only the third complete example of the monitor lizard *Saniwa ensidens* ever uncovered in the Green River Formation. At seventy-four inches in length, it is also the largest. What is more, as Lindgren points out, "it's one of the largest fossil lizards ever found in North America."

Lindgren found his extraordinary *Saniwa* during the summer of 2015. After so many years of working in the often unpredictable outcrops of the formation, Lindgren has developed something of a special sense for knowing where some of the layer's most unusual critters may lay buried.

The fact is, however, that despite all of his knowledge, Lindgren came across the lizard quite by accident—the way the vast majority of material within the formation is found. His bulldozer was removing huge sheets of rock in the hopes of uncovering large fish ... or perhaps something more special. But after one such run, Lindgren looked down and thought he saw something unusual sticking out of the torn stone. He stopped to investigate.

When he first began looking through the rock pieces that covered the lizard his heart both raced ... and sank. All he could initially see was the ghostly outline of bone lurking underneath a thin layer of matrix, yet from the size and shape he knew right away that he'd found something unusual. Still, he feared the specimen had been irreparably damaged. Either way, he knew he had an arduous task ahead of him.

Because of the potential importance of the lizard discovery, Lindgren immediately decided to suspend all other digging operations within the quarry. His attentions were then focused solely on the jumble of fossil-containing rock before him and making sure that not even the most delicate piece of skeletal bone was left behind. To enhance his efforts in that regard, Lindgren and two friends constructed a 250-gallon water tank on location, eventually attaching it to a fine mesh screen. The completed contraption was designed to function like an old-time gold sluice, allowing the team to run even the smallest pieces of surrounding matrix through the screen, filtering off debris in the hope of leaving behind dark-colored bone. At times the weeks-long process proved frustrating, often only producing a single small bone as the culmination of a day's labor. But in the end, this somewhat unconventional process proved to be highly successful, and over 95% of the lizard skeleton was eventually recovered.

"You take up these rocks in large sheets," Lindgren explained, "and by the time we saw the first evidence of bone, we had run over some of those sheets with the dozer. We didn't really damage the skeleton, but we did break the matrix into pieces. Then we set up the process for recovering any scattered remaining bone. It took us a long time. But we believe that effort was more than worth it."

Following months of careful sifting and examination, what Lindgren and his team ended up with was a giant fossil jigsaw puzzle ... without many end pieces.

Rather than be discouraged, Lindgren began attacking the overwhelming project of reassembling the skeleton with vigor, viewing the opportunity as the ultimate chance to prove himself not only as a world-class fossil finder ... but also as a world-class fossil preparator.

Dozens of pieces, ranging in size from a few feet to virtually microscopic, were carefully arranged on a table in Lindgren's lab, located not far from the quarry.

There he began the meticulous process of preparing, cleaning, and reassembling his find. It didn't take him long to realize that his discov-

Specimen of Saniwa ensidens *held in the Field Museum of Natural History in Chicago. Photo by Smokeybjb. Licensed under a Creative Commons Attribution-ShareAlike 3.0 Unported (CC BY-SA 3.0) license.*

ery was going to surpass his expectations. The bone preservation was magnificent, and except for missing a few scattered pieces around the hip joint and tip of the tail, it was all there! Even the skull, with its distinctly pointed snout, was virtually intact, though it had been twisted so that the lower jaw had become somewhat displaced. Still, this specimen represents perhaps the most complete and detailed example of a monitor lizard ever found in the formation.

As previously mentioned, two other examples of such lizards have been found in the Green River Formation. One, found in 2007, is of an apparent juvenile which features soft-tissue preservation of some scales and cartilage. The other has been, until now, the most "famous" *Saniwa ensidens* specimen ever found in these layers—a fossil currently housed in Chicago's Field Museum. That one shows a forty-two-inch lizard seemingly captured in a "swimming" position surrounded by fish, its long tail (twice the length of the body) trailing behind it.

The discovery may also prompt paleontologists to answer a very basic question: How did a monitor lizard end up being buried at the bottom of a lake some 50 million years ago? Did it wander into the water by accident in the pursuit of prey? Was *Saniwa ensidens* actually semi-aquatic? Even with this amazing new find, scientists may never know the answer to this intriguing natural riddle. Still, a number of institutions have already expressed interest in acquiring the specimen with the intent of unlocking more of its secrets before putting it on public display.

For his part, Lindgren is determined to find the proper home for his Eocene treasure. He knows that for as long as he may continue to mine the rich fossil layers of the Green River Formation, he may never come close to finding anything else as dramatic, beautiful, or valuable as his magnificent monitor lizard.

"Each specimen found adds something to the scientific knowledge of this species," Lindgren said. "The fossil in the Field Museum is magnificent, and the small one that was found in 2007 is amazing because it does have some of the fossilized soft tissue intact. But this example is special because of the size, the preservation, and the detail. I may be a little prejudiced, but I think it's the nicest and most important one ever found."

— Andy Secher

A super-sized softshell turtle (4'1" from head to tail), *Trionyx* sp., from the Tynsky Quarry. Skyler Phelps Collection. Photo © Lynn Fischbeck; used by permission.

Society of Vertebrate Paleontology to Sue to Block Reductions to Grand Staircase-Escalante & Bears Ears National Monuments

On December 4, 2017, President Trump announced that he would make large cuts to Grand Staircase-Escalante and Bears Ears National Monuments in Utah. Scientifically important paleontological resources motivated the creation of both monuments. High priority is therefore given to inventorying and protecting their paleontological resources and special funding is available for researchers who work on monument property.

SVP, in collaboration with several partner groups, will be taking legal action to block Trump's cuts. Not only do we believe that key paleo resources will be endangered when they are removed from the monuments' boundaries, but we believe that the President lacks the legal authority to reduce those boundaries. Loss of monument status endangers funding streams for paleontological research and exposes sites to damage or destruction from multiple-use activities,

PRESS RELEASE

which could feasibly include ranching, mining, or shale gas extraction.

SVP's concern for the integrity of these monuments grows out of our mission to "support and encourage the discovery, conservation, and protection of vertebrate fossils and fossil sites." Our Society has advocated for protection of vertebrate fossils on US federal land since the 1980s, culminating in the Paleontological Resources Preservation Act of 2009. Regulations under this act have still not been published by the Department of Interior.

Maintaining the scientific integrity of the monuments is a high priority for SVP. Society members were active proponents for the establishment of both monuments because of the unique paleontology that is now protected within their boundaries. Approximately 10% of SVP members have either actively engaged in long-

Paleontological and Geological Resources
Excluded from Grand Staircase-Escalante National Monument

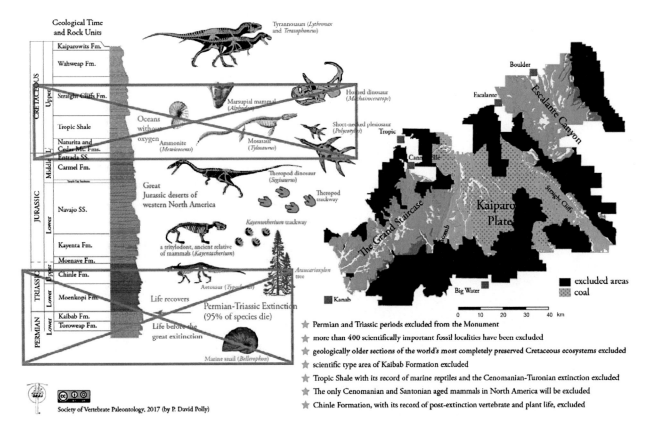

★ Permian and Triassic periods excluded from the Monument

★ more than 400 scientifically important fossil localities have been excluded

★ geologically older sections of the world's most completely preserved Cretaceous ecosystems excluded

★ scientific type area of Kaibab Formation excluded

★ Tropic Shale with its record of marine reptiles and the Cenomanian-Turonian extinction excluded

★ The only Cenomanian and Santonian aged mammals in North America will be excluded

★ Chinle Formation, with its record of post-extinction vertebrate and plant life, excluded

term research at the Monument or have made short-term research visits for field trips or site visits. Of the fifty-six authors in the 2013 volume about Kaiparowits paleontology at Grand Staircase, twenty-eight were SVP members. Similarly, twenty-seven out of the thirty-five scientific papers published in the last year about the paleontology of Grand Staircase were authored by SVP members.

Cuts at Grand Staircase-Escalante

Grand Staircase-Escalante National Monument (GSE NM) was established in 1996 in large part to preserve the unique fossils that had been discovered there over the preceding decade. Twenty additional years of research have pinpointed more than 3,000 scientifically important fossil localities at GSE NM. The monument is perhaps best known for its exquisite preservation of Late Cretaceous ecosystems. The Kaiparowits, Wahweap, Straight Cliffs, and Tropic Shale formations include one of the most diverse large herbivorous dinosaur faunas in the world, some of the only Cenomanian- and Santonian-aged mammals anywhere, and the earliest mosasaurs. GSE NM also preserves the type section of the Permian-aged Kaibab Limestone, key Triassic faunas from the Moenkopi and Chinle formations, as well as the largest

petrified forest outside Arizona and extensive trackways from the thick sandstone formations of the Jurassic.

If the maps leaked [during the last week of November] accurately describe Trump's revised boundaries, the cuts will have a severe impact on paleontology at GSE NM. Those cuts will excise the following resources from the monument, thus removing important research funding streams and many forms of protection:

· more than 400 scientifically important paleontological sites;

· the type area of the Permian Kaibab Limestone;

· all of the Permian and most of the Triassic units;

· large expanses of the Triassic petrified forest in the Circle Cliffs region that was named in the 1996 proclamation as one of the reasons for establishing the Monument;

· virtually all of the Tropic Shale, including all of its most fossiliferous exposures, which record the anoxic-driven Cenomanian-Turonian extinction, the geologically oldest mosasaur, missing links in the origin of polycotylid plesiosaurs, and the turnover between pliosaur- and ichthyosaur-dominated oceans to the polycotylid- and mosasaur-dominated seas of the late Cretaceous;

· a third of all fossil mammal sites have been ex-

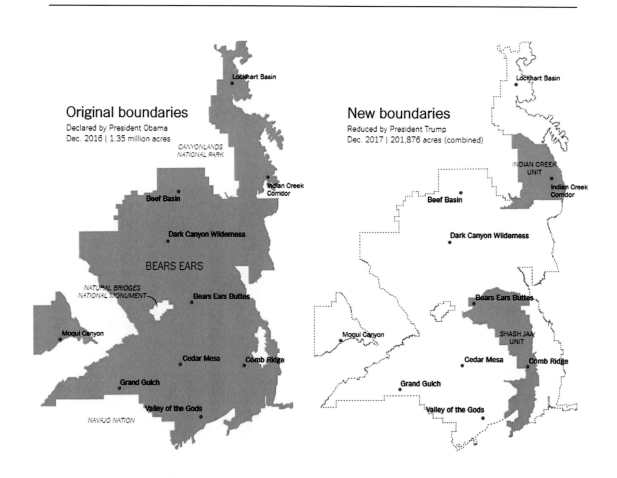

cluded, including the unique mammal sites from the Santonian and Cenomanian that were one of the primary reasons the monument was created in 1996;

· some of the most important sites in the Wahweap Formation, which was also highlighted in the 1996 proclamation, will be excluded, including the type locality of the ceratopsian *Machairoceratops* and a new species of nodosaur.

Cuts at Bears Ears

Bears Ears National Monument was established only in December 2016, following a long history of advocating by Native American tribes, conservationists, and scientists. Bears Ears is in the southwestern part of Utah near the Four Corners area. While paleontological research has been carried out there for more than ninety years, the short time that Bears Ears has enjoyed monument status means that it has not yet been as extensively studied as GSE NM. Nevertheless, Bears Ears has the potential to be as paleontologically spectacular as Grand Staircase. Bears Ears is stratigraphically older. Extensive exposures of the Pennsylvanian- and Permian-aged Cutler Group preserve some of the oldest terrestrial vertebrates, as well as highly fossiliferous sites that document vertebrate ecosystems before the Permian-Triassic mass extinction. The Triassic-Jurassic transition is especially well preserved in the Red Canyon and Indian Creek parts of the Monument, and the Jurassic sections near Monticello and Blanding, Utah have produced many important finds, including the prosauropod *Seitaad*.

If the leaked maps are accurate, the cuts to Bears Ears will reduce the monument to a fraction of its current size. Those cuts will exclude most of the scientifically important paleontological resources from monument-status:

· all of the Pennsylvanian marine units will be excluded;
· the Pennsylvanian-Permian transition in the lower Cutler Group, which is notably exposed in Valley of the Gods, will be completely excluded;
· a site in the Cedar Mesa Sandstone that preserves an ancient Permian log jam which trapped an amphibian (*Euryops*) and asynapsid (*Sphenacodon*), a site that has already suffered from extensive looting, will lose its monument protections;
· a massive new Triassic bone bed at Fry Canyon, which has also suffered from looting, will be excluded;
· unusual Triassic vertebrate burrows will be cut;
· the youngest part of the Monument's section will be excluded, including all of the Cretaceous outcrops of the Naturita Formation that have produced important angiosperm floras;
· widespread Quaternary sites, including cave faunas, pack rat middens, and floras will be excluded.

If You Conduct Research at GSE NM or Bears Ears, Let Us Know

If you conduct research in areas of either monument that are slated to be cut, please let David Polly know at svp_president@vertpaleo.org. This information is useful for documenting how reductions to the monuments will affect SVP and its members.

What's to Come

SVP will be monitoring the status of the Monuments over the coming days and weeks. If the cuts above are made, we will join with our partners in filing law suits aimed at blocking the administration's actions. First-class legal support is being provided to SVP on a *pro bono* basis by two of the nation's top environmental law firms. The cases we have assembled rest on the arguments that the President does not have the legal authority to reduce the boundaries and that such reductions will negatively impact the scientific mission of both monuments and thus the research carried out by SVP members.

As new developments emerge, we will keep you informed. Information and links will be posted on the SVP website at http://vertpaleo.org/What-is-Vertebrate-Paleontology/Fossil-Preservation-Law-in-the-US.aspx.

Thank you to all the SVP members who have come together to assemble the information needed to develop our legal case and to produce the maps and other documents that support it. Even though the review of the monuments has threatened our science, the collaborative spirt of SVP's members is tremendously heartening, and our collective knowledge is truly world class.

Sincerely yours,

P. David Polly	President, SVP
Emily J. Rayfield	Vice President, SVP
John A. Long	Past President, SVP

For more details and to follow updates, go to vertpaleo.org.

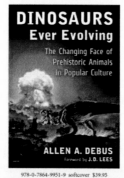

Made in the USA
San Bernardino, CA
14 May 2019